WINTER

Lindy needed the job at Whitecliffs as governess to little Danny. But Scott Wardell thought she was too young, and had no hesitation in telling her to go home. But when he changed his mind and agreed to give her a month's trial, Lindy wondered whether she was wise to stay on, especially with the beautiful Cheryl making her opinion only too obvious . . .

Books you will enjoy
by MIRIAM MACGREGOR

THE MALVERN MAN

Julie needed a holiday—so she went to stay with her cousin. Unfortunately, her cousin worked for Adam Malvern—Julie's father's arch-rival, and Adam was not too pleased to find her exercising his precious horses . . .

CALL OF THE MOUNTAIN

Lisa hadn't the slightest wish to renew her unsatisfactory relationship with Paul Mason—but how could she convince Brett Arlington of that? And why was it so important that she should?

WINTER AT WHITECLIFFS

BY

MIRIAM MACGREGOR

MILLS & BOON LIMITED
15–16 BROOK'S MEWS
LONDON W1A 1DR

First published in Great Britain 1986 by Mills & Boon Limited

© Miriam Macgregor 1986

Australian copyright 1986 Philippine copyright 1986 This edition 1986

ISBN 0 263 75498 7

Set in Monophoto Times 10 on 10½ pt. 01–1086 – 56274

Printed and bound in Great Britain by Collins, Glasgow

CHAPTER ONE

LINDY FARRELL yawned as she sat in the bus. The pale wintry sun, suprisingly warm for so late in June, filtered through the vehicle's windows to wrap her in a glow that made her feel drowsy. The slanting rays of afternoon emphasised the golden glints in her light brown shoulder-length hair, and cast shadows beneath the dark lashes framing her flecked-hazel eyes.

She fidgeted wearily, then glanced at her watch. Good heavens, it was three o'clock, she'd been in the bus for more than four hours. It was no wonder she felt tired. Then, leaning her head against the high seatback, she thought about Steve Langley.

Steve would be at the Waipawa bus depot to meet her. It was inconceivable that he would *not* be there because he'd *promised*, and from the depot he'd drive her to the Whitecliffs property which lay out in the back country near the foothills of the Ruahine Ranges. She turned and stared westward to where the mountains stretched in a seemingly endless chain along New Zealand's North Island.

There was so much that was elusive about Steve, she realised as the image of the tall sandy-haired man rose before her mind's eye. Had she been too impetuous in accepting the job he'd offered? After all, what did she know about Steve apart from the fact that he was a distant relative of her neighbours, the Hunters?

She had met him through her closest friend, Judith Hunter, but after she'd made a foursome by going out with Judith, her boyfriend and Steve, a warning had been uttered.

'Don't let him set you on fire,' Judith had said

5

laughingly. 'Steve Langley isn't the most reliable man in the world.'

Lindy had brushed the words aside. She wasn't losing her heart to him, at least, not yet, but she enjoyed his company, mainly because he made her laugh. And heaven knew she needed all the cheering up she could get because she was going through a period of depression. Mr Waite, the elderly accountant for whom she'd worked, had died of a massive stroke and she'd been thrown into the ranks of the unemployed.

And then had come the offer of the job, but apart from the fact that it involved a small boy and his school lessons she knew very little of what would be expected of her. Nor did she know anything about small boys. And as for dealing with a child's school lessons, her experience was nil.

However, this particular small boy would not be a complete stranger to her, and she became aware of an intangible motherly instinct that made her long to see him again. In fact her decision to take the job had little to do with Steve, she told herself firmly. It was the boy who had really called to her.

She recalled the first time she'd seen him. He'd been a mere bundle, a woollen-shawl-wrapped cocoon being carried up the front steps of the Hunters' house. Through her bedroom window she'd heard the taxi which had brought Adrianne home from Wellington Hospital where baby Danny had been born, and a short time later Judith had taken her in to see the little one.

'We mustn't stay too long,' Judith had whispered. 'Adrianne's not very well. She's got a queer sort of heart, something to do with rheumatic fever when she was a child. That's why she came to Wellington to have the baby. There's a special doctor here.'

'How long will she stay with you?' Lindy had asked.

Judith had looked vague. 'I don't know. Until she's stronger, I suppose, and then she'll go home to Napier.

She's another of Mother's distant relatives, something like Steve. You met him when he drove her to Wellington.'

Lindy also recalled meeting Steve for the first time, nor had she forgotten his lazy smile as his blue eyes had rested upon her. 'I suppose Adrianne has a husband somewhere?' she asked, not wishing to discuss Steve.

Judith's eyes had flashed. '*Somewhere* is the word,' she'd hissed angrily. 'According to Mother he deserted Adrianne soon after they were married, so please don't mention the baby's father.'

Adrianne Reid, a pale fragile blonde of twenty-five years, had stayed with the Hunters for almost a year. Under kindly Mrs Hunter's care her health had improved, while the baby had grown to be chubby and cuddlesome. Lindy and Judith had adored him, while Adrianne had been delighted by the attention showered upon him by the two teenage girls.

Lindy's knitting needles had clicked as she'd made him a pair of blue woollen leggings with matching jacket, the latter being in moss stitch which had needed extra care. Adrianne had been pleased with the gift, although Lindy feared he would soon grow out of it because it fitted snugly but with little to spare. Nevertheless she felt she had done something for the baby whose mother was so pale and delicate, and whose father appeared to have left them both to the mercy of others.

But all that had been five years ago. Lindy had been eighteen and she was now twenty-three, while little Danny was now ready to begin school. However, her reminiscences had emphasised the feeling that he would not be a stranger to her, and once again she became aware that her previous association with him had been the main incentive behind her desire to accept the job offered by Steve Langley.

At least, this was what she assured herself until a

surge of honesty forced her to admit that Steve himself *had* made more than a *tiny* contribution towards her decision. She'd met him several times during the last five years, and although each time had been a pleasant evening when he'd taken her out to dinner, he'd told her little about himself.

There was no accounting for the strange way in which events occurred, she mused. Steve had been making one of his periodic visits to Wellington when Mr Waite had died, and he'd done much to sweep away the gloom into which she'd been plunged. And it had been at the end of this particular visit that he'd offered her the job. His blue eyes had held a speculative gleam as he'd asked,

'What sort of a schoolteacher would you make?'

The question had taken her aback. '*Schoolteacher?* A very poor one, I imagine. Training is necessary for that sort of work.'

'Not in this case. Hundreds of back-country mothers have put small children through their first lessons. You could do it with one hand tied behind your back. If I go home without having made arrangements for a teacher of some sort Scott will become all agitato.'

'Who is Scott?'

'Oh, we run Whitecliffs together,' he'd muttered vaguely.

She'd thought about it, and realising the small pupil would be the boy she'd known as a baby, she'd been unable to resist the offer.

The intercom crackled as the bus driver's voice swept Lindy out of her reverie. 'Just coming into Waipawa——'

The heavy vehicle crossed a long concrete bridge spanning a river, then drew up at a small depot situated beside a garage. Lindy dragged her coat from the rack above her head, then peered through the window for a glimpse of Steve. There was no sign of him and she decided he could possibly be a few minutes late.

Fifteen minutes later he had still failed to appear and she was a lonely figure waiting outside the depot. The bus had departed and, sitting on the seat, she tried to calm her rising concern. A worried frown creased her smooth forehead. Surely he hadn't forgotten she was due to arrive today? Or had she made a mistake concerning the day of her arrival? Friday was definitely the day he'd arranged.

A vague feeling of unease coupled with bewilderment began to form like a ball of ice in her stomach while the question of what to do now raked about in her brain. But actually there was little she could do except remain where she was, her two suitcases beside her.

Another ten minutes passed, and then a dark blue Citroën left the bridge and swept into the garage adjoining the depot. It stopped beside the petrol pumps and a tall dark-haired man got out to speak to the attendant. He then strode towards the office of the bus depot, glancing about him in a searching manner although barely sparing a flicker of interest in her direction.

Moments later he stood before her. 'Is it possible you're Miss Farrell?' he rasped, frowning.

'Yes, I'm Lindy Farrell.' She looked up to meet a pair of dark grey eyes that appeared to be flecked by steel. They were surveying her with what she could only recognise as angry surprise. 'Who are you?' she felt compelled to ask.

'Wardell,' he retorted curtly. 'Scott Wardell.'

She was puzzled. 'Is something wrong, Mr Wardell? I expected Steve Langley to meet me.'

'No doubt. Unfortunately one can't always rely on Steve. If he has other fish to fry he grabs the pan right smartly.'

'I don't understand, Mr Wardell. Steve *promised* to be here. Where is he?'

'At the moment he's in Napier. Eventually he saw fit

to ring and tell me you'd be arriving on the afternoon bus, but he took his time about it, a fact which made me late in getting here. We're thirty miles out towards the ranges, you understand.'

She looked at him anxiously, his vaguely antagonistic attitude causing her own manner to remain formal. 'Then shouldn't we be on our way?'

'I'm afraid it'd be rather pointless.'

She was bewildered. 'Pointless? I'm sorry to be so obtuse.'

He regarded her puzzled face. 'An explanation appears to be due to you, but we can't discuss it here. Would you like a cup of tea?'

'That would be nice,' she said faintly, wondering what there was to discuss. Why didn't he put her two cases into the boot of the Citroën and set off for home?

He said, 'There's a tea-room a short distance along the street. I'll leave the car here in the meantime, and then I'll see if I can find you a room for the night— either in the one and only pub or in the hotel.'

Her jaw dropped slightly. 'Are you saying I've taken this long journey for nothing? Five hours I've sat in that bus——'

'I'm afraid so.' His mouth had become set in a grim line. 'You can thank Steve and his inability to follow a few simple instructions. I'll put your cases in the office of the depot.'

She watched as he picked them up as though they were featherweights, and moments later she was quickening her pace to keep up with his long strides as they made their way towards the tea-room. And with every step she felt more and more bewildered, knowing that here there was something strange, something that was quite beyond her understanding.

It put her into a state of being unable to touch any of the food in the glass cabinets, and as she sat at the table her hand shook slightly as she poured the tea. At the same time she examined his face, noting his straight nose and the crease in his left cheek. His square jaw denoted determination, and although his mouth was firm there was a touch of sensuality about it. Her eyes were riveted upon it when his next words startled her.

'How well do you know Steve?'

'Not very well,' she admitted. 'I've met him on various occasions when he's been in Wellington. Actually he's taken me out a few times.' She stopped abruptly, annoyed with her runaway tongue for having admitted this fact.

'Do you consider yourself to be engaged to him?'

The question amazed her. 'Of course not.'

'Good. It makes things less complicated.' His eyes narrowed slightly as they appeared to bore into her own. 'Is it possible that you're rather keen on Steve, that you have hopes of a closer association?'

Her chin rose. 'My hopes are not your concern, Mr Wardell,' she retorted coolly, knowing that any warm feeling she'd held for Steve had been considerably dampened since her arrival.

'I'll admit they're not my business—however, I can understand the sparkle in those hazel eyes catching Steve's attention.'

The compliment surprised her. 'Thank you for the kind words. I must say they amaze me. Until now you've been making me feel as though I'm covered in spots or show symptoms of a plague.'

'I assure you it was quite unintentional. You can put it down to the shock of discovering a girl of your age instead of the middle-aged woman I expected to meet. How old are you?' he demanded abruptly and without any beg-your-pardon.

'I'm twenty-three. How old are you?' she countered.

'Thirty. I'm an old man.'

'Quite ancient,' she agreed. 'What has my age to do with the situation?'

'Plenty. Mrs Price will be most disappointed. She's my housekeeper and I've promised her someone nearer her own age, a mature person with whom she might find interests in common, instead of which——' He paused and fell silent.

'Instead of which she'll find herself landed with a chit of a girl, or almost,' Lindy finished for him. 'Is that all you have against me?' she demanded wrathfully.

'It's enough, isn't it? Mrs Price is buried in the backblocks because her husband is our general handyman who milks the cow and attends to the garden. It's an isolated place where she has little or no contact with women of her own age because she's unable to drive a car, and I'm merely doing my best to keep a good housekeeper happy.'

Lindy was puzzled. 'Didn't Steve know about this age requirement?'

His voice became hard. 'He knew all right, but naturally he was looking after his own interests rather than those of Ellie Price.' He sent her a searching glance. 'Have you been to bed with him yet?'

Her eyes widened, then flashed golden sparks of anger as her cheeks flamed. 'My God, you've got a damned nerve. How dare you ask such a question? You're positively insufferable. No, I have *not* been to bed with him, nor with any other man for that matter.' She stopped suddenly, furious with herself for having divulged that piece of information, then added hastily, 'Not that it's any business of *yours*, but to think that I've travelled for hours in a bus to be insulted by such a question!' The stream of words came hissing as her anger mounted.

'Okay, okay, you can simmer down.' The grey eyes glittered with amusement. 'You're even more attractive when you are mad,' he drawled.

But Lindy found difficulty in simmering down. Tears pricked her lids and before she could control them her eyes filled. She snatched a handkerchief from her handbag, dabbed hastily and blew her nose.

'I'm sorry,' she mumbled. 'I haven't shed tears since Mr Waite died.'

'May I ask who Mr Waite might have been?'

'He was my dear, kindly old boss.' Her eyes filled again as her mind swept back to the day of the funeral, giving her a vision of the church, the flowers, the business associates in dark suits. If Mr Waite hadn't had his massive stroke she wouldn't be suffering this present humiliation. She'd be working happily in her old office.

'Mr Waite was the headmaster?'

The question amazed her and for a moment she gaped at him. 'Headmaster? No. He was an accountant.'

He frowned. 'Let's get this straight, Miss Farrell. What is your previous experience?'

'My experience?'

'Yes, in schoolteaching, of course.' He sighed as though finding difficulty in controlling his impatience. 'I presume you've had some experience in the educational world? How long have you been pumping knowledge into children?'

She swallowed then took a deep breath. Sooner or later he'd have to learn the truth and it might as well be now. 'I haven't done it before,' she admitted, looking him straight in the eye.

The dark brows drew together. 'I beg your pardon?'

'I'm not a schoolteacher,' she informed him calmly. 'I haven't come here laden with certificates to prove years of training, but Steve was sure I could do the job.'

'*Steve* was sure? That's damned brilliant.' His eyes had narrowed to thin black slits. 'You can forget anything Steve had decided. It's easy enough to follow *his* trend of thought.'

'I don't know what you mean,' she snapped, her spirits sinking lower with every passing moment.

'Work it out for yourself,' he drawled in a sardonic tone. 'You might've been stand-offish in Wellington, but after a short time at Whitecliffs he'll expect you to thaw towards him.'

'Why should he expect that, Mr Wardell?' she demanded coldly.

'Because a girl of your age wouldn't agree to go to the backblocks unless she had some sort of feeling for a man.'

She looked at him wordlessly, knowing that what he said was true. Steve *had* been seeping into her thoughts more than she cared to admit, and she'd been looking forward to seeing the place he'd referred to as Whitecliffs, the place he called home. But now she realised that any feeling she'd had for him had died before it had been allowed to blossom. Not the most reliable person in the world, Judith had warned.

The man sitting opposite said, 'Well, that wraps up the situation. I'll find you a room for the night and you'll be able to catch a Wellington-bound bus in the morning. You'll be compensated financially, of course.'

'Thank you for nothing,' she snapped. 'I've never experienced such an anticlimax.'

'What really concerns me is your lack of integrity,' he gritted harshly, his eyes the colour of pebbles.

'My *integrity*? How dare you?' She sat up straight, glaring at him as her anger boiled.

'It's a fact that you've come here posing as a schoolteacher, yet having had no experience whatever. You've come here under false pretences.'

'You're mistaken. I'm not an uneducated person, surely I can teach a five-year-old boy his first figures and letters. Thousands of mothers in back-country areas have done it for years.'

He shook his head, refusing to be placated. 'No

doubt it's a pity to disappoint you, but you'll be able to see Steve during his next visit to Wellington. He loves taking trips to the city and I'm sure he'll have explanations of some sort. He always does.'

Frustrated, she hissed, 'I couldn't care less about Steve, although I'll admit I'm terribly disappointed at not being able to see Danny again.'

A flash of interest lit the grey eyes. 'Again? What do you mean by again? Where and when did you ever see Danny?'

'I saw him every day during the first year of his life. The first time was the day Adrianne brought him home from Wellington Hospital, a mere scrap with a red face.'

He looked at her incredulously. 'You knew Adrianne?'

'Yes. She was living with the Hunters who are our neighbours. Judith Hunter and I were at school together. We've been close friends for years, but these facts can't possibly interest you, Mr Wardell. Shall we go and find a room in the hotel?' She stood up and regarded him loftily.

'Sit down.' His tone was abrupt.

She met his gaze squarely. 'Why? I've got your message loud and clear. I know you're anxious to be rid of me.'

'Not until I've heard more about Adrianne's period in Wellington. She told me so little.'

Her lip curled as she met his eyes steadily. 'Are you likely to believe me, considering my integrity is non-existent?'

'It's possible I was somewhat hasty with that assumption,' he admitted grudgingly. 'Perhaps I overlooked Steve's persuasive powers which can be quite strong at times. Did you not find this to be so?' He flashed a smile at her for the first time.

She looked at him in silence, irritated as she recalled

those same persuasive powers and the fact that she herself had succumbed to them. Her tone became brisk. 'Very well, what would you like to know? I'll tell you anything I can.'

He became thoughtful, then asked quietly, 'Do you recall the state of Adrianne's health? Did she have any bad turns when she was with the Hunters?'

'Are you asking if her heart trouble made itself felt after the birth of the baby?'

'Yes. It caused her to stay in Wellington for such a long time. It was necessary for her to be near the specialist.'

'She was very pale and thin, yet I don't recall hearing of any frightening turns—although there were days when Mrs Hunter became worried and made her stay in bed.'

'She was delicate from childhood.' His voice held a note of sad reminiscence.

'Mrs Hunter cared for her as if she were a fragile piece of Dresden,' Lindy assured him. 'She was upset when she knew Adrianne had died. We all were.'

'I'm not surprised. Everyone loved Adrianne.'

'And we all loved the baby. Judith and I took turns in nursing him.' She went on to tell him all she could remember about the delicate mother and her year in Wellington, until at last she was unable to resist a question. 'Did you have a special interest in Adrianne?' she asked gently.

'We were always good friends. She lived with her aunt in Napier but often stayed at Whitecliffs before she came to live with us.'

'I understand you were related.' Lindy put the question tentatively, not wishing to appear too curious.

'That's not entirely correct. Steve was her second cousin but I was no relation at all. Steve and I are stepbrothers, his connection to Adrianne being through his mother, who was my stepmother. Can you fathom that lot?'

'Yes, easily.' She regarded the handsome face across the table. Now that his antagonism towards her appeared to have abated she became conscious of a strange desire to know more about him; therefore she asked hesitatingly, 'You lost your own mother?'

'She died when I was six. I can remember her quite well.' He stared at the table, then confided reluctantly, 'Three years later my father married a widow with a son a year younger than myself.'

A smile lit her face. 'So then you had a mate.'

'We tolerated each other reasonably well between fights. We still do,' he grinned.

She was shocked. 'You and Steve fight?'

'No. I mean we still tolerate each other. I put up with the fact that he's not to be relied upon, that he comes and goes when it suits him, and he's resigned to the fact that Whitecliffs belongs entirely to me.'

'Oh.' She looked down at her hands thoughtfully, recalling that in some subtle manner Steve had given her the impression he was a part owner of the Whitecliffs property, but this, apparently, was untrue. Then, raising her eyes to his, she asked, 'Your father and stepmother are still there?'

'No. After Dad's death my stepmother bought a seafront house in Napier. Steve visits her quite often.'

'I'm sorry you've lost your father as well as your mother,' she said softly, her eyes full of sympathy.

He looked at her for several moments before he said, 'It was a tractor accident. Dad was discing the ground in a hilly field when the tractor side-slipped and rolled as he went round a knoll. He was pinned beneath it for ages before we found him, and although we rushed him to the nearest hospital he was so badly crushed he didn't survive the journey.'

'You've had your share of losses, and then there was Adrianne's death.' Strangely, she longed to comfort him.

'She also died at Whitecliffs. She was found on the riverbank at the foot of a cleft in the cliffs, but whether she'd been taking a short cut down, or trying to scramble up, we'll never know.'

He fell silent as the trauma of that day appeared to repeat itself in his mind. She waited patiently for him to continue and at last he said, 'It was her death that made me feel so deeply for the boy. It brought back the loss of my own mother, and I could see myself in poor bewildered Danny. It was enough to make me take him under my wing.'

'I'm surprised that Steve's mother didn't do that. After all, she's his relative.'

'Steve's mother, or Lorna, as we call her, is too busy playing bridge or going to golf. She didn't want her wings clipped by a small boy. In fact she declared she'd done her share of caring for young lads and had no intention of starting all over again. Actually, she's not keen on children.'

'Poor little Danny,' Lindy murmured, her heart going out to a small boy who appeared to be unwanted by his mother's relative.

'And then there was Ellie Price,' Scott Wardell went on to explain. 'Ellie had become very fond of him and pleaded for him to be left at the farm under her care. As for my own feelings about the matter, Adrianne and I had always been close friends, and as she'd died on my property I felt a responsibility towards the boy.'

'I can understand your feelings,' Lindy said. 'There was something very appealing about Adrianne.' Had he been in love with her? she wondered. And then his next words seemed to confirm this suspicion.

'The memory of Adrianne haunts me,' he admitted gruffly. 'I'm determined to do my best for her boy.' It was almost as though, having started to talk about her, he now found difficulty in stopping.

'I think I can understand,' Lindy said softly.

'No, you can't, you haven't a clue.' He stood up abruptly. 'We'll go back to the car.'

'But shouldn't I be finding a room for the night? I noticed the hotel on the corner.'

'No. I've decided you'll come home with me.' His long strides were taking him towards the garage.

'But that means you'll have to bring me all the way back in the morning,' she protested.

'I've changed my mind about that also. I've decided to give you a trial. We'll make it a month.'

'Well, that's big of you, Mr Wardell, mighty big indeed,' she retorted scathingly.

'At least it should please you,' he commented drily.

'Only because it will enable me to be with Danny. Otherwise, after the reception you've given me, I'd prefer to go straight back to Wellington.' She was almost breathless from the effort of keeping up with him but she managed to pant, 'May I ask, what's made you change your mind?'

He paused to stand still and face her. 'I've reconsidered the situation,' he informed her bluntly. 'The fact that you knew Adrianne could possibly enable you to have a little extra patience with Danny. He's no different from other small boys who are apt to be disobedient and who throw the odd tantrum.'

'No child is perfect.'

'And then there's Danny himself. At this moment he's probably up in the tower watching for me to bring home someone who'll read stories to him, someone who'll teach him his letters and figures. I'm not keen to face the disappointment in his eyes if I return empty-handed. Do you understand?'

A sudden laugh escaped her. 'Of course I understand. And I can also see that beneath that hard exterior you're as soft as butter.'

'Like hell I am,' he growled.

A short time later her cases were in the boot and

she'd taken her seat beside him in the Citroën. They left the town by crossing the long concrete bridge, then turned sharply right to follow the river along a road that wound between hills. Glimpses of the willow-bordered water were seen until they topped a rise that gave a panoramic view towards the distant ranges.

An inward excitement gripped her, the true reason for it being difficult to pinpoint, although she assured herself it had nothing to do with the handsome man sitting beside her. Yet she was vitally conscious of his presence as from the corner of her eye she watched his tanned well-shaped hands resting lightly on the steering-wheel, and the length of his legs stretching towards the controls of the car.

Pondering upon her inner exhilaration, she decided it stemmed from a sense of new adventure. She was about to become a governess, even if only for a short time. The word had an old-world flavour which hinted of earlier times, and she knew that before the days of the school bus many of the backblock families employed a governess for their children.

The thought made her ask, 'How did you get to school when you were very young? Or did you have a governess?'

He shook his head. 'No, my mother drove me to school, then collected me later in the day. This went on until I was old enough to ride to a corner where I left my pony in a paddock, then caught the school bus. At present that system is out of the question for Danny because he's too young.'

'And there's nobody to drive him?'

'Would I be taking you home if there were?' he asked drily.

She bit her lip, annoyed with herself for having asked such a stupid question.

He went on to explain, 'As I said, Ellie Price is unable

to drive a car. As for the men, we're all too busy to have our time broken into by school hours. So you can see the situation.'

'Very clearly. You make it sound remote.'

'For some it's been far too remote.' There was an edge to his voice that betrayed a subdued irritation.

'Are you saying it was too remote for Adrianne?'

'Oh no, Adrianne loved the place. If she'd been here there'd have been no problem as she'd have driven Danny back and forth.'

She looked at him curiously, sensing an underlying bitterness still clinging to his words. Had someone he'd loved refused to live in the backblocks? Forcing a light tone she said, 'Is there *real* isolation? I'd have thought that fast cars had made the backblocks a thing of the past, at least in this small country.'

'One could be forgiven for assuming that fact,' he agreed, then fell silent as he stared straight ahead.

Peeping at him she noticed his jaw had tightened and that his mouth had become grim. And as she had no wish to break into angry thoughts that might bring a sharp response, she occupied herself by gazing at the landscape which was dotted by weeping willows, lines of tall bare Lombardy poplars and shelterbelts of evergreen pines and macrocarpas. Yet through her thoughts the question continued to niggle. Who had found Whitecliffs too remote?

Slowly they drew closer to the misty blue-grey ranges, and as they did so the foothills with their high green pastures became clearer. At the same time the homesteads, surrounded by their trees and gardens, and backed by their woolsheds and barns, became further apart. And then, as they passed a school, Scott Wardell's silence was broken.

'That's where Danny will go to school when he's a little older. Cheryl used to teach there.' The name was uttered casually.

Lindy sent him a quick glance. 'Cheryl? She's a friend?'

'Cheryl Maloney. She was friendly with Adrianne, which meant that because Adrianne was living with us Cheryl also spent a great deal of her time at Whitecliffs.'

'Which also meant that you saw a great deal of her.' Lindy smiled at him teasingly.

'I suppose you could say that,' he admitted mildly.

'Is she still teaching at the school?'

'No. I have an idea she found children to be something of a bore.'

'So where is she now?' The question slipped out.

'I understand she's living with her mother in Napier.'

Lindy noticed he was still frowning, the scowl on his face having deepened, and suddenly she began to suspect that Cheryl was the person who had found Whitecliffs to be too remote.

But if this had been so would she have spent so much of her time there with Adrianne? Or had Scott been the force that had drawn her to the place?

And what about Scott himself? Was Cheryl never far from his thoughts, or had he merely been reminded of her when passing the school? In any case, what business was it of hers, Lindy asked herself.

Yet the thought niggled and to put it to the test she said carefully, 'I'm surprised you didn't arrange for Cheryl to teach Danny. Wouldn't she be someone he knows?'

'Possibly.'

'And if she'd been so friendly with Adrianne she'd be sure to have a great deal of sympathy for Danny.'

'No doubt. But you're forgetting I'm also looking for companionship for Ellie Price. In any case I'm afraid Cheryl and Ellie never really saw eye-to-eye.'

'Oh? Why was that?'

He shrugged. 'I've no idea. I suppose you could call it

the generation gap. Cheryl isn't much older than yourself.'

His words silenced her, while the side-glance he gave her reminded her that this was one of the reasons she herself was considered to be unsuitable.

CHAPTER TWO

UNSUITABLE—unsuitable—the word spun about in her mind until she pulled herself together and began to look about the country. A subtle change had taken place, she noticed. The hilly land had become more rugged and broken, the narrow metal road had developed more twists and sharp turns as it crossed small bridges which spanned streams tumbling between deep fern-filled gullies. Even the trees seemed to have taken on a more sombre appearance, but this, she realised, was because they were mainly natives with dark green foliage.

The silence between them lay heavily until at last she made an effort to break it. 'I suppose this land was once entirely covered in native bush?'

'Yes. Most of the properties along the foothills still have patches of rimus, totaras, or kahikateas. The altitude is higher and you'll find the atmosphere cooler than on the lower levels. Did Steve warn you to bring warm clothes?'

'No, he didn't mention anything like that.'

'Winter at Whitecliffs can be chilly—but no doubt he himself intends to keep you warm.' The statement had a sardonic ring to it.

She flushed, then snapped angrily, 'I don't know what you're talking about.'

'Steve's good at keeping pretty girls warm,' he returned easily.

The words stung, making her feel an utter fool. She also had the ghastly suspicion that he was regarding her with a certain amount of contempt, and that to him she was merely one in a long line of Steve's girlfriends. She'd been gathered up for a temporary season, and

24

later, like the rest, would be dropped. The conviction that his opinion of her could be so low made her fume inwardly, causing her to stare straight ahead and grit her teeth in angry silence.

Eventually he glanced at her and said, 'You appear to be annoyed. Is it something I've said?'

'Something you've *said*? You *are* astute,' she replied scathingly. 'If you must know I find your remarks disparaging as well as humiliating.'

He made no denial. 'You can put it down to the fact that the sight of a girl like you being taken in by Steve does not amuse me.'

Her chin rose slightly. 'Who says I'm being taken in? You're completely ignorant concerning the situation between Steve and me. You're only guessing.'

He gave a short laugh. 'I know Steve. He's a smooth operator, so let's stop this bickering, shall we?'

He drove in silence for a short period, then unexpectedly reduced speed to stop the car on the grassy verge at the top of a rise. Then, pointing ahead beyond the lower flats and twisting river he said affably, 'There it is, the Whitecliffs homestead. Can you see the house standing back from those bare white faces that drop down to the water? Limestone gives them that pale colour where the river cuts into them in a horseshoe bend.'

Distance made the river look like a thread of silver. Above it, and situated well back on a large area of plateau, the wide, single-storeyed timber house with its dome-shaped central tower reminded Lindy of a great bird sitting with outstretched wings.

Scott said, 'It's really painted white, but at this late hour of the day the shadows from the bush and hills make it appear to be blue. The area of bush at the back shelters it from cold winds sweeping down from the Ruahine Ranges, but I think you'll find the heart of the house to be warm enough.'

'That's if I'm there long enough for such a miracle to take place,' she returned pointedly.

He sent her a sharp glance but made no comment as he set the car in motion. As it glided down the hill he said, 'My great-grandparents built the house, which has been added to from time to time, and naturally it's timber because they had more timber than they knew what to do with.'

She sensed his pride in the place but said nothing to interrupt his flow of information.

'It should've been placed on this side of the river, but my great-grandmother insisted upon the high ground and the view to be had from across the river, therefore a bridge had to be built. The round tower up top gave her even more extensive views round the countryside, but now it acts as Danny's playroom. I used to do my homework there. You might like to use it as a schoolroom.'

They reached a boundary fence where a cattle-grid, flanked on either side by two large stone pillars, marked the entrance to the property. The iron bars rattled as they drove over it. A short distance further on the metal road descended to cross a bridge, then rose to wind up a hill to the plateau.

As they reached the high flat land Lindy looked up at the tower in time to catch sight of a small face peering down at the car. It would be Danny, she decided, seeking a glimpse of the person who had come to teach him. No doubt he was now bounding down the stairs for closer inspection.

Scott stopped the Citroën at the front door. He carried her two suitcases up a flight of wide concrete steps and ushered her into a panelled hall where the antlered heads of deer gazed at each other with glassy eyes. Thick wall-to-wall carpet gave an immediate feeling of comfort, and the chilly air from outside was banished by interior heating that came from somewhere.

She was right about Danny. The small boy was waiting for them, sitting on the bottom step of a narrow staircase near the centre of the hall. Lindy guessed it led up to the tower.

Scott spoke to the boy in a kindly manner. 'Come along, old chap. Come and say hello to Lindy.'

He came forward slowly, a shy expression on his pale face, his slight build, blue eyes and flaxen hair reminding her at once of his delicate blonde mother.

'Can you read stories?' he asked, looking up at her.

'You can rely on that much at least.' She smiled at him, then sent an amused glance towards Scott.

'That will be the supreme test,' Scott said, 'your ability to read stories.'

At that moment a short, plump woman with grey hair came into the hall. Lindy judged her to be about fifty, and she noticed the undisguised surprise in the brown eyes that took in her own appearance.

Scott introduced them. 'Miss Lindy Farrell, Mrs Price. We all call her Ellie, so I expect she'll prefer you to do so also.'

'It's short for Eleanor. Yes, of course I'd prefer you to call me Ellie.' The woman smiled warmly, although her eyes still reflected surprise as they rested upon Lindy.

The reason for her slight bewilderment was easy to guess and Lindy felt compelled to say, 'I know you were hoping for somebody older than me, but don't worry, I'll be here for only a short time.' She smiled at the woman reassuringly.

Ellie's brows rose. 'Only a short time? You've decided already that the place is too isolated for you?'

Lindy's smile widened and lit her face. 'Oh no, it has nothing to do with isolation. It's just that Mr Wardell has made it clear that I'm most unsuitable in every way. However, he's decided to give me a trial, but I think you'll find it won't be long before he's driving me to Waipawa to catch the bus back to Wellington.'

'She's completely inexperienced,' Scott snapped coldly.

Ellie looked perturbed. 'I see. Well, in the meantime I've put her in the middle room between you and Danny. Is that all right?'

'Anything you say, Ellie,' he returned with a careless shrug.

She flashed a smile at him. 'If I had my way, young Master Scott, I'd endeavour to keep her here for a very long time.' And with that cryptic remark she led the way along a passage leading from the hall.

Scott followed with Lindy's cases which he placed in the centre of a well-appointed bedroom. Ellie began to show her the adjoining bathroom which also served the room next door, and then Danny interrupted them.

He had left them to dart into his own bedroom and now reappeared carrying a large teddy bear which he presented to Lindy. 'This is Ted,' he informed her gravely. 'He sleeps with me.'

'And there's hell to pay if he can't be found at bedtime,' Scott added as he tousled Danny's straight blond hair.

Lindy looked at the well-worn bear which was dressed in a faded blue knitted suit of leggings and jacket. The latter brought an exclamation of surprise from her. 'This little blue suit, would you believe I knitted it for Danny when he was a baby?'

She noticed Scott frown as his eyes narrowed slightly. It was almost as though he suspected she could be lying, she thought.

But Ellie showed only amazement. 'You knew Adrianne?'

'Yes. At that time I hadn't done much knitting and I had an awful job with the moss stitch which I kept getting into rib. Even when I'd finished I discovered a small place at the back of the jacket where I'd made a mistake. See, it's just here.'

Ellie peered at the place Lindy indicated. 'It's hardly noticeable, but I can see it's there.'

She noticed that Scott's doubting expression had vanished from his face and she knew that he now believed her. It was as though she'd been able to prove she'd really known Adrianne, had that been necessary, and she was thankful the blue leggings and jacket were still in existence. And above all, thank heavens she'd recalled making that mistake in the moss stitch.

He gave a brief nod as he moved to leave the room, but at the door he paused to speak to Ellie. 'Is Steve home yet?'

She shook her head. 'No, he rang from Napier to say he wouldn't be home before tomorrow evening. He also said he'd be bringing a guest who'd stay for a while.'

Scott's brows rose. 'Oh? Who would that be?'

A worried frown creased Ellie's brow. 'He didn't say. He seemed to be very—er—high-spirited, you know how he gets. There was that odd little giggle in his voice.'

'Are you saying he sounded as if he'd been drinking?'

'I wondered about it,' Ellie admitted reluctantly.

'Perhaps he's met one of his old school mates. We'll have to wait and see who turns up with him.'

Ellie said, 'I've prepared the middle room across the passage, so whoever comes can share his bathroom. It's just like this one,' she added in explanation to Lindy.

Danny, who had been quietly examining Lindy all this time, now flung his arms about her waist. Looking up into her face he pleaded, 'Please, will you read me a story now?'

Scott, still pausing in the doorway said, 'Ah, you've been accepted.' Then to Danny, 'You mustn't pester Lindy, old chap. She has to get unpacked and settled in her room. You'll get a story at bedtime.' He then sent

her a long steady look as though admitting that he also
had decided to accept her; well, at least in the meantime.

Yet there was something about the look that made
Lindy defy him, and, sending him a brief smile she said,
'Let's break the rule. I'll read him a story *now* from a
lovely new book I have in one of these cases. Now let
me see which one it's in.'

'Goody, goody,' Danny shouted. 'Ted will listen too.'

Moments later she was sitting in a comfortable chair
with the book open and Danny on her knee. The
addition of Ted made things a little awkward but she
was able to read, 'Once upon a time there was a pet
lamb named Bobo——'

She was unaware that Ellie had beamed approval
before deciding it was time she returned to the kitchen;
nor did she know that Scott's expression had become
inscrutable as he watched them for a few moments
before vanishing along the passage.

For the first few lines of the story Lindy's voice was
shaken by a slight tremor she found difficult to control.
It was almost impossible to believe she was at
Whitecliffs and that Adrianne's boy now sat on her
knee, his head resting against her shoulder. Yet it was
true, and for this much at least she had Steve to thank.

Bobo the lamb then demanded her full attention and
she had just finished the third story of his adventures
when Ellie returned to the bedroom.

Her manner became brisk. 'Now then, young man,
run along to the kitchen. Your meal is on the table,
every vegetable waiting to be eaten up.'

Danny uttered a protest. 'Aw, gee, Ellie, not yet.'

'Yes, at once. How do you think Lindy can get
unpacked when she's reading stories to you? If you
don't let her get unpacked she mightn't stay.'

Her words had the required effect. Danny's eyes
widened as he turned to stare at Lindy, then clutching
Ted he slid from her lap and ran from the room.

Ellie laughed as she took the book from Lindy. 'There you are, you can see he wants you to stay. Now then, what's all this business about being here for only a short time?'

Lindy looked at her curiously. 'Surely you understand? For one thing it's because I'm not the middle-aged person Mr Wardell wished to engage.'

Ellie looked bewildered. 'Middle-aged? No, I'm afraid I don't understand.'

'Mr Wardell expected to be meeting somebody nearer your age, somebody who'd be a companion to you.'

'Stuff and nonsense,' Ellie exploded. 'I don't need a companion while I've got my Bert. If I'd been a widow it might've been different, but as things are Bert is the only person I need. In any case it's better for the boy to be taught by somebody young. I'm sure you'd have more understanding for him than an older woman with a tight mouth and set ideas.' She paused for breath.

Lindy hesitated then admitted, 'Well, there's also the fact that I'm not really experienced in schoolteaching. Mr Wardell wasn't very pleased about *that*. I'm afraid it's really Steve's fault for not expaining these things to me, but he was sure I could do the job.'

'Ah, now I'm beginning to see the light,' Ellie said softly. 'If Steve engaged you I can understand the reason. Does he mean anything to you?' she demanded bluntly.

Lindy shook her head. 'No. I merely went out with him a few times.' She told Ellie about her friendship with Judith Hunter and explained Steve's relationship to her neighbours.

'Then you're not in love with him?' Ellie persisted, watching her closely. 'Please excuse me for being frank.'

'Definitely not in love with him,' Lindy assured her, knowing that any sparks kindled by Steve now lay within her breast like a heap of dead ashes. Was this because she'd met his stepbrother? she wondered. *Of course not*. How ridiculous could she be?

Returning to the former subject, she said, 'At least Mr Wardell has decided to give me a trial.'

'Thank heavens for that much,' Ellie exclaimed. 'A bright face like yours is just what we need round this place. I can tell you it's been mighty gloomy since Adrianne's death. It came as a ghastly shock to us all, especially to poor little Danny. He fretted until he became ill. It was pathetic to see him running about the place sobbing his heart out while he called and called to her.' Ellie's eyes filled and she dabbed at them hurriedly.

'Doesn't anyone know what really happened?' Lindy asked.

'The post mortem revealed death to have been caused by the state of her heart. Personally I think she was just taking a walk along the riverbank and happened to be near that horrible crevice in the cliff when it occurred. It was February and the river was low enough to walk along that inner bank.'

'Is it easy to climb up or down the crevice?'

'No, it is not. Scott wonders if she could've been making the attempt, but I don't believe it. Adrianne was too sensible for that sort of stupidity. Needless to say we all try to keep Danny's mind away from the subject of his mother.'

'Poor little boy,' Lindy murmured, her heart going out to Danny.

'It's easy to see he's taken a fancy to you,' Ellie pursued. 'You'll give him something new to think about, especially with school lessons, so please don't rush away too soon.'

'You're forgetting it's not up to me, and that I'm only on trial,' Lindy reminded her.

'Don't you believe it,' Ellie smiled. 'If Scott hadn't decided he'd like you to be here he wouldn't have brought you home. Now then, I'd better make sure those vegetables are being eaten instead of being sneaked into the hèns' scrap tin.' The thought sent her hurrying away to the kitchen.

Lindy began to hang her clothes in the built-in wardrobe. She knew she would like to stay at Whitecliffs for a period, the reason being entirely for Danny's sake and having nothing whatever to do with the handsome owner of the property. She felt tired after the long bus journey from Wellington, and the emotional upset of discovering herself to be unsuitable had left her feeling drained.

She peeped into the bathroom and decided a hot shower was exactly what she needed, and moments later, having slid the bolt of the door to the adjoining bedroom, she stepped under the soothing stream.

Only a short time was necessary to relax the tension of her mind, and even as she stretched herself luxuriously beneath the hot tumbling water she was gripped by the challenge of her situation. 'I'll show you, Scott Wardell,' she muttered fiercely to herself. 'I'll show you I can teach little Danny.'

Darkness had fallen by the time she was towelling herself dry, and prior to switching on the lights she went to the windows to draw the blue velvet drapes. But suddenly she paused, stiffening slightly at the sight of Scott Wardell out in the gloom of evening.

Standing on the front steps which lay to the left of the window, he gave the impression of being a lonely figure who was deep in thought. She drew back hastily before he could see her towel-draped form, but the movement of the curtain must have caught the corner of his eye because, peeping through the gap, she saw him turn to stare at the windows of her room.

His face, lit by the light streaming through the open front door, was expressionless, and she wondered if he pondered the problem of herself. Was he regretting his decision to give her a trial? Perhaps she'd find herself being driven to catch the bus back to Wellington in the morning.

She dressed hurriedly, and by the time she'd found her way along the passage and across the hall to the lounge she was feeling less despondent. She'd taken extra care with her make-up, and the cream woollen dress that fell in soft folds seemed to reflect and emphasise the golden flecks in her hazel eyes.

She found Scott standing before the logs blazing in the fireplace, a glass of Scotch in his hand and apparently waiting to present her with a sherry. The grey eyes swept a glance of appraisal over her then rested for several moments on her lips before he spoke.

'I believe you've made a conquest; two conquests, in fact.' The words were accompanied by a slight smile.

'Oh?' She looked at him wonderingly.

'Yes. Not only with young Danny, but with Ellie as well.'

She regarded him steadily. 'Surely you're exaggerating.'

'Not at all. Ellie's opinion of my middle-aged schoolteacher-companion idea has come through loud and clear. She declared that such a person would be inclined to exercise her superiority, while she herself, being merely the housekeeper, would be made to feel inferior. I can tell you, she was not amused.'

Lindy sipped her sherry. 'She might be right. Unattached middle-aged women can be difficult, especially schoolteachers.'

'She also declared she'd be used as a listening post for the woman's aches and pains, to say nothing of her life history. I was even expecting her to declare that the unknown female would be sure to cast sheep's eyes at her Bert, but I think she realised she had me convinced. In other words, I'd got the message.'

Lindy laughed. 'She's sure I won't indulge in any of these irritating habits?'

'Apparently not. She's delighted with you.'

'Isn't it a little too soon for her to be—delighted with me?'

'Ellie's very shrewd. She says you'll make her feel young again. It'll be like having Adrianne back.'

'I see.' She found herself looking at his broad shoulders. How often had Adrianne rested her head against them? Then searching for words she said, 'Well, that should solve the companion problem. It only remains for me to prove myself as a teacher, despite my lack of experience.'

He put his glass down. 'Perhaps you'd like to see the schoolroom. It's in the tower.'

He led her into the hall, then switched on the stair light before guiding her up a narrow flight to an octagonal-shaped room situated above the hall. As he flooded it with light she saw that it contained a table, two chairs and a desk, as well as a box of Danny's toys; and apart from one section of the wall holding a blackboard, a cupboard and a bookcase, the room was surrounded by windows that gave extensive views towards hills, valleys and river flats, or to the distant bushclad mountain ranges.

Peering out at the dark indefinable landscape she said, 'I'll look forward to seeing it in sunshine.'

He moved to the door and switched off the light, plunging the room into darkness. 'It can also be intriguing by moonlight,' he said as he returned to her side. 'Look over there.'

Even as he spoke her eyes went towards a fiery crescent that developed into an orange ball as it rose beyond the silhouette of the eastern hills.

'The rising moon is always worth a few moments of our time, especially when it's almost full,' he observed softly. 'I've watched it from this window many times. Soon it'll sail aloft like a silver dollar.'

For Lindy the moments held a quality of magic, and

she became acutely conscious of the masculine vitality of the man standing beside her. She found him disturbing, and despite the darkness she knew he'd moved nearer to her as she caught the subtle odour of a pleasant aftershave. And then, as her arm touched his sleeve, she was unable to control a convulsive jerk of nerves.

He sent her a quick glance. 'You're feeling cold?'

'No. It's really quite warm up here.'

'There's a heating system of pipes from a boiler. They run through the entire house to take the chill from every room.' He moved away from her abruptly and the moments of magic began to disappear until suddenly they were completely shattered as light flooded the room.

Danny stood in the doorway, his hand still reaching towards the switch. He was clad in his pyjamas and his blue eyes looked appealingly at Lindy. 'I want to hear more about Bobo. You said you'd tell me about Bobo and the hole in the hedge at bedtime.'

The small laugh Lindy uttered was shaky from the tension she still felt, and somehow it was a relief to follow Danny as he bounded down the stairs ahead of her.

Scott went towards the lounge but turned to speak to the boy. 'One story only, Danny. Do you understand? And then Lindy will come straight back to the lounge for her second sherry. That's an order.'

And indeed it was. But he was in the habit of giving orders, she realised, and she, with the rest of the household, would be expected to obey. Nor was it any wonder he'd taken a dim view of Steve's action in employing her. Steve had been informed of the type of person Scott desired and he'd defied him by offering the job to her.

No doubt Steve would be in trouble when he arrived home. Was this why he'd failed to meet her and was now taking his time to appear? Perhaps he was shrewdly allowing Scott to simmer down or become used to the sight of her before showing his face inside the door. And even then he'd be accompanied by someone who might help parry Scott's wrath. This friend would be one of their male school friends, she presumed.

When she returned to the lounge another sherry stood waiting. She smiled her thanks, then said, 'He's a darling boy.'

Scott scowled at the amber liquid in his glass. 'I wish I could catch up with his darling father. It would do me a power of good to wring his neck. Actually, I'd like to adopt the boy. I'm sure it would please Adrianne. There are times when I see her looking at me through those blue eyes of his.'

'You're still grieving,' she reminded him gently. 'It takes a long time to get over the loss of a loved one.' She hadn't meant to utter those final words but somehow they'd just slipped out.

His response was unexpected. 'Please don't make the mistake of imagining that Adrianne and I were in love with each other. If that had been the case she would never have married Daniel Reid. Our relationship was like that of a brother and sister who always got on very well together. We were fond of each other, but I assure you, it was purely platonic.'

She looked at him wide-eyed. 'Oh, I see. Please forgive me, I thought you must've been——'

'Lovers?' He supplied the word drily. 'We were not, but I suppose your assumption is easy to understand.'

'I'll admit I did jump to that conclusion,' she said with a burst of honesty.

'Did Adrianne ever mention my name when she was in Wellington?'

'No, at least not to me. But she may have spoken of you to Judith, who spent much more time with her.'

'I doubt it. During that period her thoughts would be full of that rat, Reid, wondering where he was.'

'Doesn't anyone know where he is, even now?'

'We haven't the slightest clue. Nor do I expect him to turn up to claim his son. He doesn't appear to be obsessed by his responsiblities towards the poor little blighter.'

'I don't think Danny can be looked upon as a poor little blighter,' Lindy defended. 'He's more than fortunate to be under your wing.' She stopped, feeling slightly confused by her own runaway tongue.

'Thank you for the confidence,' he said with a wry grin. 'It'll help you to understand that I want the best for him.'

'Like someone with schoolteaching experience,' she observed with an edge to her voice.

At that moment Ellie came in to inform Scott that the dinner trolley had been wheeled into the dining-room, and if they wished to enjoy a nice hot meal would he please take Lindy to the table as soon as possible.

So he had not been in love with Adrianne, she realised as she followed him into the adjoining room with its large mahogany table and surrounding chairs. The knowledge caused her spirits to rise, and suddenly she knew she was hungry, especially when Scott lifted the lids of dishes containing a tasty venison goulash, and baked and green vegetables.

'We always serve ourselves,' he explained. 'Ellie pushes the trolley in but I won't allow her to wait on table. Nor, except at breakfast, do Bert and Ellie eat with us. They have their meals in the kitchen which gives them privacy and a time together.'

'It's a large house for Ellie to keep in order,' Lindy observed.

'She can have help whenever she wishes,' he told her briefly. 'We have two married couples on the place, and both wives are happy to earn a little extra money when the windows need cleaning, or when we have visitors in the house.'

'You often have house guests?'

'Not so frequently these days. Steve's mother used to fill the house with her friends from Napier, but that's a thing of the past. However, Steve appears to be bringing one of his mates home tomorrow night. I can't imagine who it'll be.'

The evening passed quickly because Lindy went to bed early, or perhaps it would be more accurate to say she was ordered to bed early.

'You've had a long day,' Scott said as the mantelpiece clock struck nine-thirty. 'You'll be ready for a good night's sleep.'

'Yes, I'd like to feel fresh to begin with Danny in the morning.'

'Aren't you forgetting that tomorrow is Saturday? School doesn't begin until Monday. Even your limited experience in schoolteaching should tell you that the schools are closed on Saturdays and Sundays.'

She felt nettled. 'Of course I'm aware of the weekend holiday—but in this case does it matter?'

'Yes, it matters. Danny must begin by learning school routine. Your hours will be from nine till three with breaks for playtime and lunch. And I'm sure you'll need these breaks——'

'Who's teaching this boy?' she asked, tempering the words with a smile.

He ignored the question. 'Tomorrow morning I'll show you round the house area. One particular place is definitely out of bounds for Danny, and you'd be wise to know where it is in case you see him heading in that direction. I'm referring to the crevice in the cliffs.'

'Oh yes, where Adrianne——' She fell silent.

'Exactly. I don't want him to go near the place.'

'I'll keep him away from it,' she promised.

'Correction.' He looked at her mockingly. 'All you'll be able to do is your *best* to keep him away from it—the little imp.'

Later, as she lay in her bed she made an attempt to review the events of the day. The long bus journey from Wellington had almost vanished from her mind, and even Steve's failure to meet her at the depot had faded into insignificance. But very real was the memory of Scott Wardell's antagonistic attitude when he realised she was not the type of person he had expected to meet, although he was at least giving her a trial. Her eyes closed and she slept soundly.

Next morning she was awakened by the barking of dogs. A horrified glance at her watch sent her springing from the bed, and after a quick shower she pulled on a pair of green and red tartan trews with matching green jersey. She then made her way to the kitchen where she found Danny finishing a plate of porridge.

Ellie turned as she entered. 'Ah, there you are. Just sit at that table. Breakfast is usually in the kitchen. I'll give you a plate of porridge.'

'I only have a slice of toast at home,' Lindy protested.

'Do you indeed? You'll get out of that bad habit while you're here,' Ellie declared flatly. 'It's himself that says we're all to start the day on a good breakfast and porridge is what he advocates. You just wait till you try it with brown sugar and cream. Besides there's the example to be set for his nibs, here.'

Lindy didn't argue. She found the porridge delicious and was enjoying her tea and toast when a sturdily built man came into the kitchen. Nor was it difficult to guess that this was Bert Price.

He removed a knitted woollen cap to reveal a bald head, and as Ellie introduced them his twinkly blue eyes ran over her slim form. 'Well, I'll say this much for

Steve,' he said at last, 'he sure knows how to choose a good-looking girl.'

'There now, you're making her blush,' Ellie said as she refilled Lindy's cup.

Scott entered the kitchen a short time later. He sent Lindy a cool penetrating stare, his eyes lingering on the moulded curves beneath her green jersey. His glance then moved towards her feet.

'Have you a pair of rubber boots?' he asked.

'Yes.'

'Good. Put them on. We'll be walking on wet grass. And a warm jacket if you have one. Despite the sun it's chilly outside because there's been a frost.'

A short time later she presented herself for his approval, thankful that she'd brought a duffle coat and the required boots. Then, as they turned to leave the kitchen, Danny's voice rose in an agitated demand. '*I want to come too.*'

'Not this time, old chap,' Scott told him firmly.

Ellie said, 'I'll be baking this morning. Would you like to make something with a nice piece of dough?'

Danny stamped his foot. '*No*, I want to go with Uncle Scott and Lindy.' The tearful wail followed them as they left the house. '*I wanna come, I wanna come,*' he yelled from the back door.

Scott swung round and shouted, '*Daniel*, stop that racket or there'll be no stories today.'

Silence followed the threat, but moments later a small face peering at them from the tower indicated that their progress was being followed.

Scott led Lindy across the yard and into the field to where the dog-kennels were sheltered by the spreading boughs of ancient macrocarpa trees. Beyond them were two sheds. The first held a land cruiser while the second contained agricultural equipment, and here he explained the various functions of the tractor plough, the harrows and discs for working up the ground and the drill for sowing the bags of grass-seed standing against the wall.

He then pointed across the field to where two red-roofed houses nestled among trees. 'We call them the staff cottages,' he explained. 'Eric Briggs, our shepherd, lives in the one on the right. He's in charge of two thousand breeding ewes. Jake Lomas is in the other cottage. He's our deer man.'

She misunderstood his meaning. 'Your *dear* man?'

'As in stags and hinds. We have two hundred breeding hinds and about half a dozen stags.'

'Oh, I always think of sheep and cattle on farms, but then I'm just a city girl.'

'Farming is expanding in New Zealand. Deer are no longer looked upon as vermin to be hunted in the ranges. They're now captured and farmed, the venison being exported overseas. At one time we had a herd of Hereford cattle but it's been replaced by red deer, which are more profitable.'

'Whitecliffs must cover a large area,' she remarked hesitantly, not wishing to appear too curious about the extent of his property.

'Five thousand acres,' he replied nonchalantly, 'but that includes areas of bush which shelter the deer during the worst months in winter. The stags like trees. They rub and polish their horns against the trunks.'

'You appear to have your own kingdom in this wilderness,' she smiled, then immediately regretted the final word because this obviously well-organised property was anything but a wilderness. Nor was she surprised when he frowned and took her up on her remark.

'Wilderness? That means you also consider the place to be isolated?'

'I didn't say that,' she said hastily, then made an effort to change the subject. 'Didn't you say there is something I must be shown? Something important?'

'Yes, we'll go this way.'

They left the implement shed to follow a farm road that joined the main drive. A gate enabled them to enter the field lying in front of the house, and as they crossed it she realised he was leading her towards the cliff tops.

Sheep scattered as they approached the fence on the far side. She could see it had been set well back from the treacherous edges that dropped down to the river, and as there was no gate it was necessary to climb over the tight strands of wire.

On the other side a short walk took them to where a jagged break in the cliffs formed a crevice wide enough to allow a descent to be made to the river below, and, peering down, she could see the muddy water rushing past the base of the cliffs.

CHAPTER THREE

LINDY drew back hastily as the sight of the swift waters made her feel giddy. 'It's frightening.'

'Yes, but I understand it was worse before my great-grandfather had the front opened. Until then it formed a funnel. An unsuspecting person could fall down it, or an agile person could climb up by finding footholds on the sides. It's still possible to get up or down but I don't encourage this exercise. You'll understand why Danny must be kept away from this area.'

'I'll keep an.eye on him,' she promised again.

'Unfortunately there's a kind of fascination about getting up or down. It's like a challenge, or an achievement.'

'I don't believe Adrianne would make the attempt. She was far too sensible.'

'You're right. Personally I think she was walking along the side of the riverbank in a search for coloured stones washed down from the mountains. She had quite a collection of them.' He paused, then added, 'Thank you for having faith in her intelligence.'

She looked at him with compassion, knowing that this place had stirred the memory of Adrianne, and that she was never far from his thoughts. At the same time she sensed there was something about the memory of Adrianne that still worried him.

They climbed the fence again and made their way back across the field towards the gate. He then led her towards the front garden where red-hot pokers brightened the winter day by thrusting brilliant heads above their sharp-bladed foliage.

There was a seat beside a clump of spindleberry

bushes, colourful with their bright pink and yellow leaves still clinging to twigs and branches, and as they sat down Lindy took several deep breaths. 'I can understand Adrianne loving this place,' she said. 'The air is so crisp and fresh, so free from pollution of any kind. Everything is so peaceful.'

He gave a short laugh. 'Would you believe there was a time when this whole plateau rang with the yells of battle?'

'Battle?' Her eyes were wide as they turned towards him.

'It's part of Whitecliffs's history. It would probably bore you.'

'I assure you, it would not. Please tell me.' Startled, she realised that already the place was holding a fascination for her.

'Well, it all happened many years ago when the Maoris owned the land and before there were any white people in this area of the country. A tribe of natives living inland beyond the ranges were in the habit of making periodic trips to the coast for seafood which was an important part of their diet.'

'It must have been a tremendous journey,' Lindy remarked.

'I understand it was always in summer when the snow was off the ranges and the tracks were easy to negotiate. They had stopping places on the way, and this flat was where they rested for a few days before or after the arduous trek over the ranges. A good spring gave them fresh water and the high position above the river enabled them to watch for enemies.'

'The Maoris always had their enemies,' Lindy said, making an effort to show she was not entirely ignorant concerning the habits of the country's native race.

'Yes, well, an occasion arose when a band of young warriors from an enemy tribe learnt of their presence on the plateau, and this war party followed tracks along the lower land on the other side of the river. In those days it was covered with heavy bush, therefore they were kept well hidden from any watchful eyes above. They crossed the water which was low at the time, and while creeping along the narrow bank beside the cliffs they found the cave with the crevice rising up to the plateau.

'After a consultation they decided to climb up the shaft and attack the inmates of the little huts, but they were unaware that the shaft had acted as a funnel and that their voices had carried up to the man on sentry duty. Therefore, as each warrior emerged at the top he was dealt with in no uncertain manner. Those who escaped made their way back to their own people and a second war party was organised to avenge the first one.'

'Utu,' Lindy said. 'That's the Maori word for revenge. I'll bet there was a fight.'

'You're right. This time they made a wide detour and attacked from behind. The occupants were taken by surprise and despatched before they knew what had struck them. The enemy then burnt all the small sleeping huts, destroying the lot.'

Lindy shuddered. 'Such ghastly bloodshed.'

'In fact so much death that the place became tapu, or a forbidden place, and because of it no Maori would use the area again. Years later it was sold to the Government who in turn put it up for sale. When my great-grandfather bought it he began by sawmilling the timber. My grandfather continued in this line, and as the land became cleared the pastures were sown. Further development was carried on by my father—until his death—and now it's my turn to carry on the good work.'

'And after you?'

He shrugged. 'I suppose it'll be Danny, unless I can find sons of my own.'

'You don't appear to be in any hurry.'

'I've been too busy to do much searching,' he retorted drily, then, almost as though deliberately inspecting her as a possible applicant for the position, he turned to examine her.

A dull flush rose to her cheeks as the grey eyes slid over her features one by one. They held her gaze briefly, then moved to the soft sweetness of her lips before resting on her throat. From there they glided to the rounded curves of breasts beneath the green jersey, now plainly visible because the unfastened duffel coat had fallen wide open.

She stood up abruptly. 'I'll admit I find it all—er—quite interesting. I can understand your reluctance to leave the place, even for the all-important job of finding yourself a wife,' she added lightly.

'Some day she'll come to me,' his deep voice drawled.

'You're sure of that? Well, when she does happen to arrive, good luck to you both.' Then, by way of changing the subject she asked, 'Would it be possible to see some of the deer?'

'Of course. We'll go after lunch.'

'Danny may come with us this time?'

'If you wish. Then certainly he may come.'

'I'd like to spend plenty of time with him before lessons begin,' she explained, although this was only part of her reason for wanting Danny to be with them. In some strange way she imagined the small boy's presence would help keep her mind on an even keel and away from the hypnotic appeal of this man's personality. And although she told herself her imagination was running away with itself she was vitally conscious of an urgent need to keep her feet on the ground.

Later, when lunch was over, Danny shouted with excitement as the Land Cruiser was driven to the back door. 'Ted says he wants to come too,' he declared, clutching the bear as he climbed into the rugged four-wheel-drive farm vehicle.

'I hope he asked politely,' Lindy smiled.

The little boy looked at her with serious eyes. 'He's a good teddy. I heard him say *please*, Danny, may I come too?'

Lindy laughed and hugged him.

Scott gave an amused grunt. 'Sometimes I wonder exactly who dictates Danny's activities, the adults or that bear.'

The Land Cruiser followed a well-laid metal road, crossing fields and winding between hills until they came to a large enclosure where red deer hinds grazed with their fawns.

Scott stopped to enable Lindy to alight, and as she walked across the grass she gazed up at the lofty poles supporting the strong netting fence that was more than six feet in height.

'Deer can leap over the average fence,' Scott explained. 'I'll see if I can coax a few of them to come a little closer.'

As he lifted two buckets of barley from the Land Cruiser the nearest animals raised heads on long necks to watch him carry it through a nearby high netting gate. They became aware of the line of golden grain being spread along the grass, then stepped forward daintily on slender legs. Large moist eyes gazed at them, then a row of wet black noses went down to the grain.

Moments later the sound of an approaching motorcycle floated on the quiet country air. It was ridden by a man a few years older than Scott, and as he pulled up beside them he said, 'Everything okay, Boss? I saw the Land Cruiser and just wondered.'

'Yes, they're all grazing calmly.' He introduced Lindy. 'This is Jake Lomas—Miss Farrell.' Then to his deer manager he added, 'Miss Farrell is to be Danny's teacher. They're just getting to know each other before school begins Monday morning.'

Jake swept a pair of keen eyes over Lindy. 'Is that a fact?' he drawled, a sly grin spreading over his weather-beaten face. '*Danny* and the young lady are getting to know each other, are they? Well now, isn't that interesting.' He stared intently at Scott, his widening grin seeming to imply he knew exactly who were getting to know each other, and that it had little to do with Danny.

Lindy felt her cheeks go hot. She turned away to stare at the hinds with their coats gleaming redly in the wintry sun, and she heard Danny say, 'Ted's coming to school, too.'

'And what about Uncle Scott, is he going to school, too?' The ring of amusement still echoed in Jake's voice.

But before the subject could go further Scott switched to the feeding of deer and the weight of stags.

Jake said, 'I've been waiting for Steve to come home. I'd like him to give a hand in culling a few of the older stags.'

'He'll be home this evening,' Scott told him. 'He's bringing a mate who might be glad to assist for the sake of the novelty.'

'And I need his help with some fencing,' Jake added. 'So if you'll ask him to get in touch——'

Scott nodded and they watched as Jake wheeled the bike round, revved the motor and rode away. He then said, 'Would you like to see the arena and yards where we hold the deer sales?'

'Yes, please, I'd like to see everything.' She was afraid to sound too eager but was unaware that her eyes sparkled with interest.

The Land Cruiser took them past the next high-fenced enclosure inhabited by weaner hinds, and beyond it was a raised three-sided structure of tiered seats attached to a windowless shed.

'That's the deershed,' Scott informed her. 'Light filters in through slits at the top of the walls, and the inside gloom helps to quieten the animals before they come out into the arena or saleyard. Auctioneers stand on that platform while buyers look down on the animals from the seats.'

While Scott explained the deer sale procedure Danny amused himself by running along the seats and jumping from one to the other until Lindy feared he'd fall and hurt himself. She caught him as he raced past, then turned to Scott anxiously. 'This place is dangerous for him. I think we should leave it.'

'You're right,' he agreed. 'I'll take you to the woolshed. Have you ever seen shearing machines or a woolpress?'

She shook her head. 'I'm almost ashamed to admit that this is the first time I've been on a farm. It's an entirely new world.'

His mouth gave a cynical twist. 'But you hesitate to admit that it could soon become much too boring?'

'On the contrary,' she returned quietly. 'I suspect that involvement with animals could become quite fascinating.'

The remainder of the afternoon was spent in a state of easy companionship, and as they drove back to the homestead Lindy knew that the isolation of Whitecliffs would never hold any fears for her. Thinking about it she realised that one hour's drive would take her to Napier, and from there an hour's flight with the domestic air service would enable her to visit her parents in Wellington.

But, glory be, where was her mind leading her? These questions would never arise because her time here must be limited. And after all, she was here only on trial, wasn't she? The thought made her turn to Scott with a question.

'How long do you intend keeping Danny at home? He must go to school eventually, you know.'

'I'm well aware of that fact. However, the situation

depends upon the transport problem of getting him to school and home again. In the meantime his education must not be allowed to lag behind.'

When they reached home they found Ellie setting four places on the dining-room table, a reminder that Steve and his friend were expected in time for dinner. Well, it was no great deal, Lindy told herself as she attended to Danny's bath. She'd remain her usual friendly self and Steve would soon realise she couldn't care less about his broken promise to meet her at the bus.

Later, after she'd showered and changed into a melon-pink dress that sent warmth to her creamy complexion, she found Scott waiting for her in the lounge. He looked arresting in a bottle-green jacket and light bone-coloured trousers, and after handing her a sherry he poured Scotch for himself.

As they sipped their drinks in silence she became acutely aware of the grey eyes taking in every detail of her appearance.

'That's an attractive dress,' he remarked at last. 'The colour does something for you. It'll have real impact on Steve.' There was a twist to his mouth as he uttered the final words.

'But not on *you*. Is that what you're trying to say?' she flashed at him, then mentally chided herself for allowing the words to slip out.

He stared into his glass and said nothing for several moments, then, glancing at his watch, his voice came smoothly. 'The moon should be really full this evening. Shall we go to the tower and watch it rise?'

Without waiting for her to reply he took her glass and placed it beside his own on the mantelpiece, then, taking her arm, he led her from the room and up the stairs.

She went like an obedient child, and as they reached the tower she wondered what his reaction would have been if she'd refused to accompany him. At the same time she had to admit there was something exciting about watching the moon rise in the company of this man, and she knew that her heart was beating a little faster.

He switched off the light and they crossed the room as the orange curve began to peep over the distant skyline of hills, and as he'd predicted, the moon was now really full. Within a short time the surrounding valleys and rises were lifted from utter darkness to be transformed into places of shadowed mystery.

Beams slanting through the tower windows washed them with a subtle light, and in the dim glow she became aware that his eyes were upon herself rather than on the moonlit panorama stretching below them.

Searching for words to cover her embarrassment she said, 'From this vantage point one's imagination could run riot.'

'You feel that too?' he asked quietly. 'When I was a boy I used to creep up here on clear nights when the moon was full. That line of Lombardy poplars down on the river flats became a row of tall soldiers. I used to stare at them, waiting for them to march forward, but they never did.'

She gave a low laugh, feeling more at ease. 'I suppose those round-topped willows near the water would've been their camp?'

He moved closer to her, placing one hand on her shoulder as he pointed with the other. 'Do you see the gap opening into the gully on the right? I used to wait for enemy troops to rush from it, but they never appeared.'

His nearness, and the pressure of his hand on her shoulder, caused her to draw a sharp breath but she remained calm as she looked up at him with understanding. 'No doubt you were the general who commanded operations from up in this tower?'

'I suppose you could say that,' he admitted without removing his hand from her shoulder.

Still conscious of its pressure she said, 'But at last you had to go to bed.'

'With a flea in my ear after I'd wakened the entire household by shouting commands from the window.'

She laughed. 'And now the time has come when you can shout commands all over the place and they'll be obeyed.'

'In most cases, apart from the odd exception.'

She looked at him quickly. 'You're referring to Steve?'

His hand dropped to his side as he said, 'As I told you before, Steve comes and goes as he pleases. He gets paid for the work he does on this property, but an income left to him by a doting grandmother has enabled him to be fairly independent.'

She veered from the subject of his stepbrother by saying softly, 'I'm glad you confided those intimate childhood memories to me. It's like sharing a secret, and when I leave this place you can be sure I'll respect your confidences.'

Despite the darkness of shadows reflected in his grey eyes she knew he was regarding her with a slightly puzzled air. 'I don't know what got into me,' he mused at last. 'Would you believe I've never spoken of them before? They've been locked inside me for years, yet somehow you managed to drag them out. How did you do it?'

She shook her head vaguely. 'I've no idea, unless it was sparked off by the suggestion of imagination. I pointed out that it could run riot, remember?'

'Imagination can be dangerous. It can lead one along the wrong path,' he declared harshly.

She tried to fathom his meaning but was unsuccessful. Was he warning her against imagining that Steve had any intention of settling down with one woman? 'Many things can be dangerous,' she parried lightly.

'Like moonlight. Did you know that moonlight can be dangerous?' His words were now spoken in a low deep tone.

Again she wondered at his meaning, and again she shook her head vaguely as she said, 'I've never found it to be dangerous.'

'It's inclined to make a lovely woman look even more beautiful and to deprive a man of his sanity. Common sense he's been trying to hang on to suddenly goes by the board.'

'You mean he becomes—moonstruck?' She kept her tone light.

'Something like that. It's a sort of madness.' His hands went to her shoulders, turning her to face him.

Surprised, she looked up into his darkened features, her pulses quickening from the pressure of his fingers, and then her heart began to thud as she felt herself being drawn closer to him. She realised his arms were enfolding her slowly, as though waiting for her to resist his embrace, but she was also conscious of the magnetism that emerged from his male strength, wrapping itself about her like a cloak and transforming her into a willing puppet.

Then, just as slowly as his arms had enfolded her, his head bent and his lips found hers. It was a kiss that sought a response from her, gentle at first and then teasingly sensual as his arms gathered her close to the tautness of his body.

And before she could gather her wits or control her actions her arms had crept about his neck. Dear God, she thought, was it only yesterday she'd met him? Had her mind also become influenced by the moon's rays?

It had to be the answer because there couldn't be any other reason for the delicious tingling that raced through her veins while his arms pressed her against the lean contours of his thighs. Nor could there be any other reason for her own rising desire that made her heart thud in her throat, and, of their own accord, for her soft lips to become parted beneath his kiss. It was almost as though her spirit was reaching out to meet his soul—but surely the moon couldn't have such an effect.

Suddenly her stomach felt strangely hollow while sensations that were foreign to her began to sweep her into a mindless state where she floated in a cloud of ecstatic bliss. Strength from him seemed to flow through her, pumped into her spinal cord by the gentle kneading of firm fingers on her back.

His lips left her own to nuzzle her ear, and without releasing her he murmured, 'What the hell are you doing to me, Lindy?'

A small shaky laugh escaped her. 'What am *I* doing to *you*?' She hid her face against his neck. 'How would I know?'

'Don't be naïve. You must know you're stirring the very devil in me. You're awakening something that's deep down inside, something that's been asleep.'

How could she admit he was stirring similar emotions somewhere within her own depths? Steve had never had this effect upon her, nor had any other man, yet Scott Wardell, who had previously been full of antagonism towards her, was now moulding her against himself as easily as if she'd been a pliable piece of putty. It was as though he was about to strip her naked and possess her body. And that, her confused thoughts began to tell her, was exactly what he had in mind.

'What was it you said about being moonstruck?' she asked with a tremor in her voice.

'I warned you it could be dangerous,' he reminded her, his voice low and husky as he gathered her closer to him.

His lips found hers again, but even as his passion made itself obvious, her own thoughts became clearer until they pounded with the knowledge that this madness had nothing whatever to do with the moon. And one thing was certain, she was being a fool to allow this man to kiss her with these forceful demands that betrayed all too clearly what he had in mind. Nor must he be allowed to imagine he could cajole her into satisfying his sexual needs and desires. She would have to watch her step, and her emotions.

It was difficult, but her hands found their way to his chest while she struggled to wrench her mouth from his, and as she turned away she gasped weakly, 'Stop it, Scott, stop it at once. I don't know what you've got in mind but this is insanity.'

'Is it?' His voice was low. 'I thought it was rather nice. Somehow I got the impression that you did also. Are you telling me I was mistaken?'

'No—no——' She shook her head in a dazed manner. 'But please understand I'm not a girl for a one-night stand if that's your aim.'

'I didn't mean to give you that idea,' he protested quietly as his arms dropped to his sides.

She felt a sense of relief until his next words indicated that his first impression of her still floated about in his mind. 'I'm afraid the moon must've gone to my head because I was forgetting you're Steve's girl.'

Infuriated, she snapped at him. 'You can get that idea right out of your head. I told you before, I am not Steve's girl.' Then, still glaring at him, she was surprised to see a flicker of light cross his face, and suddenly the room brightened sufficiently to reveal the grimness of his mouth.

'A car has come over the hill beyond the river,' he said, supplying the answer to the source of the light. 'It'll be Steve and his mate. Shall we go downstairs to greet them?'

'Why not?' she answered lightly. No doubt he had visions of watching their reaction to one another, but if he expected to see her fall into Steve's arms he was due for a disappointment. In any case it mattered little what this man thought. That, definitely, was a fact. Or so she assured herself.

They made their way down to the lounge, where Scott refilled their glasses, and as they sipped their drinks they listened for the sound of the approaching car. A couple of horn blasts at the front door announced its arrival, and moments later Steve came into the room.

He was accompanied by one of the most beautiful girls Lindy had ever seen. A tall redhead, she had green eyes, full sensuous lips and a figure to be envied by the most glamorous of models. The skirt she wore fell from a neat waist to emphasise slim hips, while the matching top plunged to reveal the cleavage between full rounded breasts.

Steve said cheerily, 'Hi, Lindy, glad to see you got here all right, but then I knew you would.' He gave a laugh that was full of confidence as he crossed the room to where she stood near the fireplace. Taking the glass from her hand he placed it on the mantelpiece, then gave her a hug that held her a little too closely.

The action infuriated her but she kept control of her temper as she turned her lips away from his mouth.

'Hey, what's this? Where's the loving kiss I expected?' he protested.

'I think it's still waiting at the bus stop,' she snapped. Then, icily, 'Isn't it time you introduced me to your friend?' Nor was she able to meet Scott's eyes which, she felt sure, would be full of sardonic mockery.

'Oh yes, sorry and all that sort of thing, this is Lindy Farrell, Cheryl Maloney. I've told Cheryl about you, and no doubt Scott's told you about Cheryl.' The words ended on a slight laugh that held a subtle message.

Lindy forced herself to smile at Cheryl. 'Well, yes, actually he did mention your name.'

A pleased smile flashed across Cheryl's face. 'He *did*? Scott darling, does that mean you've been thinking of me?'

There was a sharpness about Scott's tone as he avoided the question. 'I merely pointed out the school where you'd taught and which Danny will attend at a later date. Now then, I'm sure you'd like a drink. Your usual, I suppose?'

'Yes, please, you always remember my usual Scotch on the rocks. You really are a dear.' She paused, then said earnestly, 'You know, I really had to *make* myself come home with Steve.'

'Oh?' Scott's dark brows rose.

'Well, it's the first time I've been here since we lost Adrianne. I was afraid that being here without her would be too—too poignant, too harrowing.'

Steve said hastily, 'Now don't go upsetting yourself. I'll bring your bags in from the car.'

Scott glanced at her sharply. '*Bags*? You've come for a prolonged visit?'

'Of course, for as long as you need me,' she assured him seriously. 'I'll find my way to my room.' She put her glass down and as she swung round to leave the room her skirt swirled about her long shapely legs. But within moments she was back, her eyes flashing like green lights as they rested upon Lindy. 'You're in my room,' she declared accusingly.

Lindy was startled. 'Am I? I didn't know,' she faltered. 'I'm in the room Ellie gave me. Are you expecting me to vacate it?'

'Yes, definitely, and at once, if you don't mind.' Cheryl softened the demand with a smile that didn't quite reach her eyes.

'Just a minute, Cheryl,' Scott intervened softly. 'Is there something wrong with the room Ellie has prepared for you?'

'Of course not,' she assured him hastily. 'It's just that

it isn't my *usual* room, the one next to *yours*,' she added
in a low undertone.

Lindy wondered if the last words spoken so quietly
had been meant for Scott's hearing alone, and for some
reason they jarred on her ears. Her thoughts flew to the
communicating bathroom and she wondered if, previously, it had served as a pathway between the two
bedrooms.

'Couldn't you ask Ellie to change us over?' Cheryl
pleaded. 'I can't understand why she didn't put me in
my usual room,' she added petulantly.

'The answer to that is simple,' Scott informed her.
'She didn't know you were coming here this evening.'

Cheryl swung round to face Steve, who had now
returned from carrying her suitcases in from the car.
'Didn't you tell Ellie you were bringing me home?'

He grinned sheepishly. 'No. I thought you'd be a nice
surprise for Scott. I wanted you to dance in while I
shouted *surprise, surprise*.'

Smiles wreathed her face. 'Oh, how very sweet of you.'

At that moment Ellie came in to tell them the trolley
had been wheeled into the dining-room. Her eyes
widened slightly as they rested upon Cheryl, but apart
from a polite acknowledgement by way of a nod she
gave no form of greeting.

Cheryl, on the other hand, was slightly effusive. 'Ellie
dear,' she cooed, 'how lovely to see you. You're looking
just as bright as ever. I'm sorry Steve didn't see fit to
tell you he was bringing me home, otherwise you'd
never have put me in the wrong room. After all, Scott
once told me to look on this place as my second home,
isn't that so, Scott darling?' She turned to look at him
pleadingly.

'That was when Adrianne was here,' Ellie reminded
her before Scott could answer. 'And now I'm sure you'll
be comfortable in her old room. I'm sure you'll like
that.'

'But Ellie dear, don't you see? We were such close friends I'll be able to feel her in there, almost as though her spirit's hovering above me. It'll be most disturbing, whereas Lindy wouldn't mind at all.'

'If Adrianne's ghost is in that room you'll be most fortunate,' Ellie told her flatly. 'You'll be able to sit and chat all night.' She turned to Scott. 'There's a leg of hogget waiting to be carved. Please don't let it go cold.'

The subject of the bedroom was dropped as they moved into the dining-room, but the discussion had embarrassed Lindy to the extent of making her feel uncomfortable. At the same time she had no intention of offering to change rooms unless she was sure it was something Scott desired, and in that case she'd have no option but to do so gracefully.

Watching Cheryl from across the table Lindy marvelled at the other girl's beauty. No doubt the lashes framing the green eyes were heavy with mascara, but it made them glow; and it was possible that much of the red hair's brilliance came from a bottle or a tube, but it caught the attention as it fell on either side of the clear complexion of her face. When compared with Cheryl, Lindy feared that she herself looked about as interesting as a poor little consumptive mouse.

And then Cheryl's previous words swam into her mind. *Scott told me to look on this place as my second home*, she'd said. The words had been spoken with quiet satisfaction and Lindy now realised that Cheryl was the one who had considered Whitecliffs to be too isolated.

Had she now changed her mind about this fact? Was her visit an attempt to rekindle whatever flame had been between them? The fire is never dead while the ashes are still red, she recalled as she looked at Scott thoughtfully. How are your ashes? she longed to ask.

Her thoughts were interrupted by Danny coming into the room. Dressed in pyjamas and clutching the Bobo book he stood beside Lindy's chair. 'You didn't read to me,' he complained with a reproachful look on his face.

'Oh, I'm sorry.' She'd forgotten about his story but didn't dare admit that Cheryl's arrival had swept it from her mind. 'Come along, we'll have a short one now.' Excusing herself she left the table and took Danny back to his room.

Scott followed her along the passage. 'This is ridiculous,' he told her impatiently. Then, to Danny, 'Look here, old chap, Lindy is having her dinner. You can't expect her to read stories in the middle of her meal. It'll turn stone cold.'

'Uncle Scott's right, Danny,' she said, knowing it was unwise to pander to the boy's demands in this manner. 'I'll come as soon as I've finished my meal.' Then, snatching at the opportunity to question Scott she turned to ask bluntly, 'Would you prefer me to change bedrooms with Cheryl?'

His face became inscrutable, 'Are you afraid I'll come charging through the bathroom? Is it that *you* want to change?'

'No, I didn't mean that. But if you *want* me to change——'

'I see no reason for you to do so,' he retorted crisply.

She felt relieved. 'Thank you. That's all I wanted to hear.'

'However, there's just one point. I presume you realise the opposite room would put you next door to Steve, with the same bathroom set-up?'

'That's why I'd rather be next door to you,' she admitted frankly. 'And with someone like Cheryl in the house you're unlikely to turn in my direction.' She was unaware of the despondent note in her voice.

'Is that a fact? So we'll leave things as they are, shall we?'

When they returned to the dining-room Scott remembered to pass on to Steve Jake's request for assistance on the fence at the stag enclosure. He then turned to Cheryl with what appeared to be an attempt at making general conversation.

'So what have you been doing since you were last at Whitecliffs?' he asked politely.

She shrugged emerald-clad shoulders. 'Oh, this and that. Very little of anything, in fact. After Adrianne's death I found great difficulty in settling down.' Leaning forward she pressed Scott's hand with her own. 'The memory of Adrianne is something that you and I will always share. Isn't that so?' She smiled at him sadly.

'I suppose so,' he muttered gruffly. 'But you haven't told me how you've been filling in your time.'

'Oh, I've had a long holiday in Auckland with dozens of parties and dances.'

His mouth twisted slightly. 'Ah, I can see you've been in deep mourning.'

'Can't you understand I had to get her out of my mind? But that restlessness is over now and I'm ready to put my mind to something more definite. That's why I'm here.'

Scott frowned at her. 'I'm afraid I don't quite get your meaning. Something definite, you said.'

'Yes, like teaching Danny. When Steve told me you'd decided to start him off with tuition at home I knew exactly what I had to do, and I came at once.'

'But didn't Steve also tell you that Lindy was here for that purpose?' Scott's tone was cool.

'Oh yes, he told me a little about her,' Cheryl returned casually. 'It was enough to make me realise she's quite unsuitable.'

The words shocked Lindy. She sat erect and glared at Cheryl. '*Unsuitable?* How dare you say that about me?'

'Of course you're unsuitable because you're inexperienced in schoolteaching,' Cheryl returned smugly. Then she sent an arch smile towards Scott. 'I presume you know that she can't possibly have a clue about where to begin.'

'Of course I knew it,' he snapped.

'And do you also know she'll be spending more time with Steve than with Danny?'

'How dare you?' Lindy exclaimed in ringing tones. 'You *are* doing your damnedest to get rid of me.'

Cheryl ignored Lindy's outburst while gazing at Scott beseechingly. 'As Adianne's *dearest* friend I felt it my duty to come and take over Danny's schooling until he's ready to go to the school bus corner. After all, *I am experienced,* which is more than can be said for some people.' The smile she sent Lindy was full of triumph.

Scott stared at the table for several moments. 'It's very good of you to have the boy's interests so much at heart,' he said at last.

Cheryl pressed home with what appeared to be an advantage. *'Naturally.* He's Adrianne's son, isn't he? What else would you expect from me?'

'However, there's one point you appear to be overlooking,' Scott informed her. 'I've already engaged Lindy. I've said I'll give her a trial. Do you expect me to go back on my word?'

'A *trial,* for how long?' Cheryl demanded.

'For a month. School beings on Monday, and at the end of four weeks we'll see how Danny has progressed.'

'I really think you're wasting your own and Danny's time,' Cheryl snapped impatiently.

Scott's shoulders lifted slightly. 'Well, we'll just have to wait and see whether or not he learns anything. Naturally, you're welcome to extend your visit for as long as you wish, but in the meantime I don't want disruptions of any sort. Lindy must be given a fair chance with the boy.'

The hard note in his voice had given Cheryl the message, and as she turned to Lindy her green eyes held a cold glitter. Nevertheless she controlled herself to the extent of forcing a smile as she said. 'Well, Miss Schoolteacher, it's over to you. I'd be interested to learn how one of your inexperience proposes to begin.' A shrill laugh escaped her.

Steve, who had remained silent during the discussion now said quietly, 'Lindy is a resourceful person. I'll bet she's got some plan up her sleeve.'

Scott's stare was penetrating. 'Have you something up your sleeve, as Steve suggests?'

'It's possible,' she replied evasively.

They looked at her in silence, waiting for further explanation.

'Have you never heard of the Department of Education's Correspondence School?' she asked quietly. 'I've come well armed with material from them. Did you really think I'd muddle along in the dark?'

CHAPTER FOUR

THE silence that followed Lindy's words was broken by Cheryl's exclamation, 'The Correspondence School——!'

Lindy smiled. 'I presume you've heard of it. The lessons go by post to children in the back-country areas.'

'Of course I've heard of it,' Cheryl snapped. 'I just don't *need* it, that's all. You're forgetting I'm *trained*,' she reminded Lindy wrathfully.

'You've taught the beginners in the infant classes?' Lindy put the question mildly.

Cheryl glanced from Scott to Steve. 'There's no need to hide that thinly veiled amusement,' she told them angrily.

'Be honest, Cheryl.' Scott's tone was dry. 'Have you ever had actual experience in the infant classes?'

'Well, no, they were all classes of older children,' she was forced to admit.

'So you're both more or less on an even footing,' Steve pointed out, 'except that Lindy has the advantage of the Correspondence School's infant lessons.'

'I've *handled* children,' Cheryl added with a note of triumph. 'I doubt that she's had much to do with them.' Her lip curled slightly as she swept a look of disdain over Lindy.

The meal ended a short time later and as Lindy began to stack the dishes Scott laid a restraining hand on her arm. He then stood up and spoke to Steve.

'You and Cheryl can attend to the trolley and push it out to the kitchen. I'm taking Lindy to the office. It's time this teaching job was put on a more definite basis.'

Lindy noticed that Cheryl's eyes glittered slightly but no comment came as she followed Scott from the room. Cheryl, she realised, had been made to understand that the two of them were on a par.

Scott led her to the end of the hall where a door gave access to a small book-lined room. There was a large desk, a cabinet that looked as if it held bottles and glasses, and she guessed that this was where the farm and household accounts were attended to. There were also comfortable chairs which seemed to indicate it was the room where business pertaining to the property was discussed.

He leaned against the desk, his arms folded across his chest. His face was unsmiling as his eyes regarded her with accusation. 'Why didn't you tell me?' he demanded abruptly.

She was nonplussed. 'Tell you what?'

'That you'd come supplied with Correspondence School lessons. You could've explained this fact when I met you at the bus.'

She regarded him steadily, her eyes wide. 'I suppose it would be impossible for you to understand that your attitude at the bus shocked most things out of my head. At that point I expected to be returning to Wellington almost immediately.'

'But didn't I say I'd give you a trial? You could've told me then, so why the secrecy?'

'There was no secrecy, as you put it. In any case I presumed a trial meant only a few days, or a week at the most, so it didn't seem to matter. Besides——' She fell silent as bitter memory took her back to her arrival at the bus depot.

'Yes? Besides what?'

She gave a deep sigh of impatience as she faced him. 'Can't you realise that my mind was in a state of turmoil? I'd been let down by Steve, who'd promised to meet me, and then I was being rejected by you. To have brought up the subject of the Correspondence School at that moment would've made me feel I was pleading to be given a chance. I am *not* in the habit of crawling to people, Mr Wardell.'

'You can cut out the Mr Wardell,' he snapped.

But she was still on her high horse and in no mood to be placated, therefore her voice rang with determination as she said, 'Incidentally, if you'd really prefer to give Cheryl the job, it'll be okay with me.' She looked away from him, knowing this to be anything but the truth.

'What do you mean? Don't you want the job? Are you backing down? You don't look like a quitter.'

'No, I am not a quitter,' she flared angrily. 'I mean that I know perfectly well that it's just your pride that persists in making you give me a trial. You've said you'll do it, and your ego will not allow you to break your word.'

'Something of a psychologist, are you?' The words came mockingly, and then he began to chuckle.

His mirth did nothing to ease her irritation. She took a deep breath and then the words tumbled recklessly. 'What I'm trying to say is, if you'd rather give the job to Adrianne's friend who is also *laden with experience*——'

'Weren't you also Adrianne's friend?'

'Yes. But Cheryl's so—so beautiful, and I'm sure you'd rather have her around.' The words faltered on her lips. Dear heaven, what was she saying? Now he'd wonder if she was jealous.

'She's certainly something to look at,' he admitted unaware that his words acted as tiny knife stabs. 'However, I didn't bring you in here to discuss Cheryl. At the moment I'd like to hear more about the Correspondence School. What made you think of it?'

'It seemed the logical course to take because I wanted to make sure I could do the job. The headquarters are in Wellington, so it was easy to contact the Principal, who was most helpful to me.'

'He decided you'd be capable?' The words came teasingly.

'Strangely, he did,' she retorted coolly. 'He explained that it's a triangular affair between teacher, pupil and parent. In this case I'm taking the place of the parent. The lessons go in special envelopes to the teachers, and are later mailed back to the students. So you won't need Cheryl's tests to learn Danny's progress, you'll be able to see it for yourself from a more official source.' Her chin rose slightly as she uttered the final words.

'So we'll just have to wait and see how he gets on.' His tone became brisk. 'Now about salary.'

Her eyes widened at the sum he mentioned, but her protests were brushed aside. 'Teach Danny to read his own stories and you'll be worth every cent of it,' he commented drily.

There was a light tap on the door as Cheryl pushed it open. 'Have you two finished discussing my little Danny's education?' she demanded petulantly. 'Why don't you do it over coffee in the lounge?' The green eyes flashed numerous questions as they slid from Scott to Lindy.

'We're coming,' Scott muttered gruffly.

As they entered the lounge Steve stood up. He crossed the room, took Lindy's arm and drew her towards the sofa. 'Come and sit beside me, Kitten, I want to know what you're been doing since we drove round the bays in Wellington.'

She glared at him speechlessly. *Kitten?* What on earth had possessed him to bring forth that infantile name? Yet honesty forced her to admit that while sitting in his car to watch the harbour lights twinkle she hadn't objected to it at all. In fact she'd rather liked it.

But now things were definitely different. She was seeing Steve in a much clearer light and the sooner he realised she was no longer his *kitten* the better she'd be pleased. Thank heavens her association with him hadn't gone too deeply.

Nor were matters helped when Cheryl made no attempt to hide her amusement. Busily playing hostess with the coffeepot, she paused to stare at Lindy. *'Kitten?'* She giggled without restraint. 'Is that what he calls you? I think it's quite laughable.' The sniggers continued throughout the pouring of the coffee.

Lindy forced herself to smile in agreement. 'Yes, it is. One can only say it's preferable to being called *Catty*.'

Cheryl's eyes narrowed as her tone changed. 'Are you accusing me of being catty?' she snapped.

Lindy merely looked at her without bothering to reply, and it was a relief when Steve repeated his question.

'You've not yet told me what you've been doing since I last saw you,' he persisted.

'He appears to be asking for a full report,' Cheryl remarked with a further touch of amusement. 'Like who has been taking you out recently?'

Lindy ignored her as she turned to Steve. 'There's nothing to report. Being free from office hours enabled me to spend time in the museum and art gallery, and I also browsed in the bookshops for anything that would help me with Danny.'

'Such as the Bobo book?' Scott put in.

'That and others to help with his alphabet and figures. You know the sort of thing, A is for apple, B is for banana. One apple, two bananas. I guessed he hadn't had the advantage of playschool or kindergarten, and that he'd be starting from the very beginning. They'll be used in conjuction with the Correspondence School work.'

'You'll be reimbursed for them,' Scott told her abruptly.

She shrugged the question aside as she turned to

Steve. 'So, what have you been doing since we watched the harbour lights?'

'You mean apart from working with stock at Whitecliffs?' He frowned thoughtfully. 'Not very much. Yesterday I went to a race meeting, and last night Cheryl and I went to the cabaret. It's on the waterfront.'

She looked at him in silence as she sipped her coffee. Yesterday he'd been to the races and then to the cabaret. Pride forbade any mention of his promise to meet her at the bus depot, and from the corner of her eye she could see Scott watching for her reaction to these admissions. Nor was she able to turn and look at him because she knew the grey eyes would be full of mockery.

Steve continued casually, 'The cabaret was great. Good floor, excellent music. We must make up a foursome and go there again.'

'Just as we used to when Adrianne was with us,' Cheryl exclaimed with enthusiasm. 'Only it won't be the same.' She sent a resentful glance towards Lindy, then turned to Scott impulsively. 'You must promise to be my partner. I won't go unless you're my partner, so *promise*.'

Scott sent her a lazy smile. 'As Steve has suggested we'll go as a quartette, but without being tied to definite partners, just as we always did.'

Cheryl's full lips pouted but she did not press the point.

Steve then changed the subject. As he stood up to refill his cup he said, 'I've left Danny's present in the car. I've bought him a kite.'

Cheryl turned to Scott. 'Would you believe he was buying him a huge bird affair? It would've lifted Danny up into the sky. I made him change it for a smaller one that a little boy could handle.'

'He'll need someone to fly it with him in any case,'

Steve said with his eyes on Lindy. 'We'll take it down to the riverflats tomorrow.'

Cheryl crossed the room to sit on a small stool beside Scott's chair. She gazed up at him appealingly. 'What will you be doing tomorrow?'

He sipped his coffee thoughtfully then said, 'The men have the day off, therefore my usual Sunday chore is to ride round the sheep to make sure none of them are cast, especially the in-lamb ewes.'

'Oh yes, they get on their backs and are unable to find their feet,' Cheryl declared knowledgeably. 'Is Meg still out there? May I ride with you?'

'Of course, if you wish.'

'It'll be much more interesting than flying a kite,' she said with a sidelong glance at Lindy. Then, hesitatingly, 'Actually, I've brought my jodhpurs because I hoped to go riding with you. Of course it would've been after school hours, but now I can go out on the farm with you all day. It'll be just wonderful,' she added happily.

'Hmm.' Scott's reponse was non-committal.

Watching them from across the room Lindy was conscious of a surge of longing. If only she could ride a horse, she thought wistfully. But life had denied her the opportunity to learn, whereas Cheryl had been blessed by many visits to Whitecliffs. No doubt she'd ridden with Adrianne, or had it always been with Scott? The answer was not hard to guess.

And now this girl with the flaming hair and perfect figure was able to use the ability to her advantage, and while she herself would be closeted in the tower schoolroom with Danny, Cheryl would be cantering over the fields with Scott. She'd be exercising every ounce of charm while supplying him with feminine companionship, which was something he'd lacked for the last few months.

Scott's next words startled her. It was almost as though he'd read her thoughts through the depression reflected on her face. 'Do you ride, Lindy?' he asked casually.

She shook her head sadly. 'No, I'm afraid not.'

'Then we'll have to teach you,' he replied.

Her face brightened. 'Oh, would you? That would be wonderful.' But her spirits fell with his next words. 'Steve can take time off to give you lessons after school hours. He takes time off for almost everything else, don't you, old boy?'

'Yes, sure.' Steve was unperturbed. 'Good idea. I'll enjoy it. Cheryl can come too.'

'No, I won't,' Cheryl snapped crossly. 'And what's more I think it's a waste of time because Lindy won't be here long enough to learn to ride well. Also, when she returns to Wellington she'll have neither a horse nor a place in which to keep it.'

'Aren't there riding schools just out of Wellington where horses can be hired?' Scott queried, his eyes resting on Lindy.

She nodded. 'Yes, and I could use Mother's car to go there at weekends.'

'Then that's settled. We'll put you up on Meg. She's very quiet and without vice of any description,' Scott replied calmly.

Cheryl uttered a protest. 'But Meg's *my* horse. I always ride her when I'm here.'

'We'll find you something else,' Scott promised with an air that closed the argument.

The rest of the evening passed in casual conversation that had no depth as far as subject-matter was concerned, and as it progressed Lindy sensed the veiled antagonism wafting from Cheryl towards her. There was nothing she could complain about openly, but the feeling that Cheryl resented her presence was so persistent she longed to leave the room and go to bed.

Even when the television was turned on she became conscious of malicious little glares being shot in her direction, and at last she knew she could stand it no longer, so she stood up and spoke to Scott. 'If you'll excuse me I'd like to go to bed. Could I borrow a book? I saw shelves of them in your office.'

Cheryl sprang to her feet. 'I'll help you find one that's interesting. Have you a favourite author?'

'There's no need for you to disturb yourself, Cheryl,' Scott informed her easily. 'They're all in order on the shelves—detective, travel, romance. I'll show Lindy the various sections.'

As he held the door open for Lindy, Cheryl's voice came sharply. 'Don't be too long, there's a good film starting soon.'

When they reached the office he shut the door then turned to face her. 'Well, do you think you can cope during this coming week while Cheryl's here?'

Lindy decided to be frank. 'Do you mean because of her attitude towards me? You must've noticed it.'

'Yes. Who could miss it? I'm afraid it's because she's jealous of the fact that you'll be teaching Danny.'

'Didn't you tell me she gave up teaching because she wasn't very fond of children?'

'Yes, but Danny's the exception. When his mother was alive she was almost part of the family. At heart she's a dear girl, but she can also be difficult.'

'You find her a *dear girl*? Then why don't you give her the job? I can easily go home on Monday and let her have it. There's no need to persist with this—this silly situation.'

'You mean she's getting under your skin? You're ready to throw in the sponge?'

'I didn't say that. But if I could feel sure she's the one you'd prefer to have as Danny's teacher I'd bow out gracefully, despite your promise of a month's trial.'

'I'll try to keep her out of your way.'

'Thank you. I'm sure she'll be excited about going riding with you, just as you'll be delighted to have her company.'

Appalled, she realised her voice had become tinged with bitterness and hoped it had failed to register with him. But at the same time she wondered why it should be there. Why should it matter to her if Scott wished to be with Cheryl? Her only concern was with Danny, wasn't it?

The thought made her say, 'There's one small point we appear to be overlooking and that is, which of us would be the better teacher for Danny. Isn't that the real question we should be considering?'

'I've already considered it,' he said briefly.

'You have? I'm grateful my own inexperience is being given a chance against Cheryl's load of experience.'

'There's more than that to my decision. There's the fact that you made an effort to do your best for the boy, such as getting in touch with the Correspondence School and purchasing books. To me it proves you had real affection for the little fellow who was next door, and for his mother. Thank you, Lindy.'

He stepped closer, bent swiftly to kiss her cheek and then her lips. His hand on the back of her head added to the brief pressure on her mouth.

His action sent the blood rushing through her veins yet transformed her into a state of immobility which caused her to gaze up at him like a hypnotised rabbit. At last she said shakily, 'I'm glad you no longer think I came here just to be near Steve.'

His hands on her shoulders, he stared down into her face. 'That has still to be proved,' he returned quietly, then his arms went about her as he held her closely against him. His cheek rested against her forehead before his lips trailed across the smoothness of its creamy surface.

She leaned against him, waiting for his lips to meet her own again, and longing for a display of passion that would equal that of earlier moments in the tower. Her pulses began to thud, and she was about to raise her face to his when suddenly she felt his body go tense. His arms fell to his sides and a swift movement took him to the bookshelf.

The next moment Cheryl came into the room. The green eyes narrowed as they slid from Scott to Lindy. 'Good grief, haven't you found a book yet?' she exclaimed.

Scott ignored her as he handed a book to Lindy. 'Have you read Daphne du Maurier's *Rebecca*? You'll enjoy it.'

She took it from him without admitting she had previously read it.

He took another book from the shelf. 'And this is something I often browse through but it would probably bore you.' He opened at random a beautifully bound volume of Omar Khayyam. 'The moving finger writes, and having writ moves on,' he read.

She finished the lines for him. 'Nor all thy piety nor wit shall lure it back to cancel half a line, nor all thy tears wash out a word of it.'

'Ah, you know Omar.' His voice rang with pleased surprise, and from the expression on his face he gave Lindy the impression he was really seeing her for the first time. Their eyes met and their gaze held as a look of understanding passed between them, but the invisible link was suddenly snapped as Cheryl gave an exclamation of extreme impatience.

'Hell's bells, give me strength. Scott *darling*, do come along,' she pleaded as she took his hand and tried to drag him from the room. 'The film has already begun.'

Watching his reaction Lindy noticed he allowed himself to be persuaded without too much reluctance. And who could blame him? she asked herself with a sense of inner depression. Cheryl was so beautiful, and apparently he considered her to be a *dear girl*.

Later, when she slid between the sheets, the urge to read left her, and instead she made an attempt to review the situation in which she now found herself. But despite all efforts to channel her thoughts her mind was unable to see beyond the image of Scott Wardell. Nor did she try to deny the fact that the man affected her in a manner to which she was unaccustomed.

Lindy woke next morning to a winter's day that was fine but chilly. Heavy clouds rolled across patches of blue, driven by a sharp breeze that guaranteed to send Danny's new kite aloft. She sprang from the bed, then showered and dressed quickly in a warm dark red tracksuit.

Nearly everyone was in the kitchen when she entered its cosy warmth. Scott and Bert Price sat in the window seat where they discussed alterations to be made to the vegetable garden, while Steve used a corner of the large table to assemble the kite. Danny watched him intently, his excitement evident, until Ellie placed a plate of porridge on the table before him.

'Eat every spoonful or there'll be no kite-flying today,' she informed him in stern tones. 'In any case I think it'll rain.' Her words died as Cheryl entered the room.

The tall redhead was like a stage heroine making an entrance. The well-tailored jodhpurs emphasised her slim waist while the bright green jersey, stretched to its utmost across full breasts, made her eyes look like emeralds. Make-up had not been spared, and around her face her hair had been back-combed and fluffed into a flaming cloud.

Scott rose to his feet and stood looking at her in silence, while Steve's eyes slid over her with a gleam of appreciation. Bert Price grinned widely, but Ellie's mouth tightened with disapproval.

Cheryl walked across the room with studied grace. She bent to kiss Danny's cheek. 'How is my little boy this morning?'

Danny's head bent low over his plate. 'Not your little boy,' he declared stolidly. 'You're not my mummy. My mummy's an angel. Ellie says so.'

'Of course she is, darling,' Cheryl agreed. 'So now you can be *my* little boy.'

'*No I won't.*' The refusal was shouted with surprising force.

There was an uncomfortable silence in the room as Cheryl left him, a slight flush staining her cheeks. 'He'll come round to accepting me,' she said with a light laugh that was not over-burdened with confidence.

Ellie brought the room's atmosphere back to normal. 'Breakfast is ready. Porridge for everyone, or bacon and eggs.'

Lindy took her seat beside Danny and began to butter his toast. She cut it into fingers, and as she did so she became aware that Scott watched her actions, his face expressionless.

Cheryl also watched with an air of thinly veiled belligerence, but suddenly it was shaken off as she sent a dazzling smile towards Scott. 'Where are we riding today? To some of our old haunts?'

The dark brows drew together. 'Our old haunts?'

'Oh, you know, to some of those lovely faraway places on the edge of the bush, or perhaps up one of the mountain tracks.'

'Nothing so romantic,' he said with an unexpected grin. 'It'll be a ride to check all the fences and to assess the materials needed for repairs.'

She pouted. 'But you have *staff* to do that sort of thing.'

'Only a fool relies entirely on staff,' he returned easily. 'The boss must be seen to be taking an interest. Besides, I like working with my men.'

'Oh, well, it'll be more exciting than *kite-flying*,' Cheryl said with a half-glance towards Lindy.

Lindy suspected that Cheryl was enjoying a moment

of triumph over her, but she managed to smile and say, 'It's years since I've flown a kite. I know I'll enjoy it.'

'Of course you will, you'll be with Steve,' Cheryl almost purred, then laughed knowingly as her glance glided from one to the other.

Lindy felt it wiser to let the comment pass although she knew Scott's eyes were upon her, and in any case, with Steve sitting beside her there was nothing she could say. Further, any sound she uttered would surely betray the irritation growing steadily within her, irritation that would reveal the fact that she was jealous. Yes, *jealous*, she realised with a shock.

Nor did the turmoil within her grow less when, a short time later, she watched Scott help Cheryl mount the grey mare known as Meg. *What the devil's the matter with you?* she hissed at herself. *You've known the man for less than two days. You're behaving like a silly schoolgirl with a mad crush on the teacher*. Yet she continued to stand transfixed, her eyes on Scott who sat his tall black mount as though he were part of the animal.

'Are you coming?' Steve's voice spoke from behind her. He carried the kite and was accompanied by an excited Danny, and as he led Lindy from the yard towards the drive his eyes followed the two riders. 'They're a handsome pair. Cheryl's had tickets on Scott for years. Maybe they'll clinch the deal this week.'

Lindy swallowed hard, then managed to ask casually, 'Why hasn't the deal been clinched before this late date?'

Steve shrugged. 'Lord only knows. However, she's a very determined girl. I reckon she'll land him in the end.'

The words infuriated Lindy. 'Why did you bring her here?' she demanded, making a valiant effort to conceal her anger.

'It was her idea. When I told her that Scott intended

keeping Danny home, at least until the end of this year, she decided that she must be the one to teach him.'

'But didn't you tell her?'

'About you? Of course I did. She blew my head off for engaging you, and then she cajoled me into promising to bring her home to talk to him about it.'

'So during this week she'll be doing her utmost to—to discredit me in Scott's eyes,' Lindy pointed out wrathfully. They had reached the bridge at the bottom of the hill and she paused to stare down at the waters that rushed and tumbled before sweeping round the bend beneath the cliffs. In a voice that had changed to one of misery she added, 'It'll be easy for her to make me look an utter fool and completely incompetent.'

Steve gave a short laugh. 'I doubt it. Believe me, she'll be much too busy exercising her charms over Scott. She'll be continually seeking his company, but that'll be a good thing for us.'

She was nonplussed. 'For us? I can't see why.'

'Of course you can, little duffer. It'll keep him occupied and leave us free to be alone. I saw this point right smartly when she was persuading me to bring her home. It was the only reason I agreed to do so.'

Danny tugged at him impatiently. 'Why are we standing on the bridge? When are we going to fly the kite?'

'As soon as we get to those riverflats, old chap,' Steve said.

Lindy's heart sank as they walked up the rise beyond the bridge. She realised she no longer wished to spend time alone with Steve, and she was thankful she'd be able to escape to the tower for lessons with Danny. And of course Steve would be kept occupied with farm work, so perhaps she was worrying unduly.

They went through a gate and he led her past the row of leafless weeping willows bordering the river. Sheep scattered as they approached a wide area of flat grassland, their small hoofs thudding as they raced towards the line of tall Lombardy poplars.

Lindy stood still as she turned to look from the poplars to the willows, and then her mind flew back to those moments in the darkness of the tower when Scott had confided his boyhood fantasies. It was easy to imagine she was standing between the soldiers' camp and the line of marching men. It gave her the strange feeling of knowing the place well. It was almost as if she belonged to Whitecliffs.

Danny's voice broke into her daydream. 'Look at the kite, it's up, it's up.' The small boy was almost beside himself with excitement until suddenly his face changed to one of reproach as he stared at Lindy. 'You didn't watch Uncle Steve run with the kite,' he accused.

'I was looking at that row of trees,' she explained, offering a lame excuse.

He turned and stared at the trees. 'Why?'

'They're so tall and straight, just like soldiers marching.'

He stared at her blankly, his lack of understanding obvious. 'The kite's best,' he exclaimed scornfully. 'It's away up there, it's higher than the trees, it's as high as the sky. Uncle Steve,' he shouted. 'I want to hold it, let me hold the string.'

He rushed across the field to where Steve held the tremendous length of string controlling a red and yellow plastic bird with long streamers for a tail. It soared to make a splash of colour against the clouds, dancing and dipping on sudden gusts of wind before floating even higher with its tail outspread.

Lindy made her way towards them, reaching them as Steve uttered a warning to an exuberant Danny. 'Hold tightly to this bar. If you let go that bird up there will fly away. It'll be lost forever. Do you understand?'

Danny nodded eagerly as his small hands gripped the short bar attached to the heavy string. Then, his expression rapt as he gazed upward, he flew his first kite.

Lindy smiled as she watched him, then she became aware that Steve had moved closer to her. His arm slid about her waist and she knew he was looking down at her. She also knew that if she looked up and met his eyes he would kiss her, therefore, determined not to give encouragement, she moved a few steps away from him.

'The kite's a wonderful new toy for him,' she said lightly. 'It was kind of you to think of it, it's making him so happy.'

'What about you, Lindy? Are you happy to be here with me?'

'Oh, yes, of course.' It was all she could find to say.

'Good. We'll have some fun together.' His tone held satisfaction as he again moved closer to her.

She turned to look at him. 'Fun? What exactly do you mean by fun?'

'You know perfectly well what I mean. We'll get to know each other really well.'

'Steve, I think I'm beginning to know you better than you realise. Much better than I did in Wellington.'

'You are? Then that makes it much easier. I *knew* you weren't a prude, you're just a slow starter.'

'What is that supposed to mean?'

'It means where *fun* is concerned, of course.' He paused thoughtfully. 'It's a pity you didn't change rooms with Cheryl and then I'd be able to slip through the bathroom so easily. I'll see if it can be arranged. She'll be delighted.' His arms again slid round her waist.

She was appalled by the suggestion, her first instinct being to yell at him in fury. However, she had no wish for open warfare, therefore she made a supreme effort to control herself. Keeping very still she allowed his arm to remain about her waist as she said in even tones,

'Steve, if your idea of fun goes beyond the bounds of *friendship*, you can forget it.'

'What do you mean?'

'Surely it's clear enough. We're friends, and I value your friendship, but that's all. During my stay here I have no intention of becoming your sexy little plaything. Is that understood?'

'No, it is not. And what's more I don't recall being aware of this attitude in Wellington where you didn't object to my arms being around you, or to my kisses. What the hell's got into you?'

She knew very well what had got into her, but she remained silent because it was impossible to explain that those evenings had occurred before she met his stepbrother, Scott Wardell.

Nor had Steve finished pleading his case. 'I suppose you're mad with me because I didn't meet you at the bus depot. I'm sorry about that, but I became tied up with Cheryl.'

She smiled sweetly. 'Well, I suppose it was reason enough to forget all about me.' *Cheryl*, she thought bitterly. She was enough to distract any man.

Steve uttered a sound of impatience. 'It's quite obvious you've got the pip with me, but you'll get over it. What do you say to beginning our relationship on a new basis starting from now? This is just for friendship.'

An unexpected movement of his arms switched her round to face him, and as he held her closely his lips descended upon hers in a kiss that was more friendly than passionate. Still determined to avoid a fierce quarrel, she was about to free herself from his arms without too much force when loud yells of distress rose on the air.

Danny had lost his grip on the kite. His new toy was floating away, dragging its long string.

Steve released Lindy and raced across the field in

vain pursuit of the dangling string holder, but it was well out of reach.

Danny flung himself against Lindy. He was sobbing loudly. 'I fell over,' he gasped tearfully. 'The string stick jumped out of my hands.' He buried his face against her and wept bitterly.

'Never mind, darling, we'll buy another one,' she consoled.

'Don't want another one, want *that* one,' he howled.

'Hush darling, perhaps it'll come down in a field, it might not go too far.'

'It'll go to heaven,' he wailed. 'Like my mummy.'

'No it won't, oh, look, Danny, the string has caught in one of the poplar trees. The soldiers have caught it in their arms. Uncle Steve will be able to save it for you.'

His sudden silence enabled her to hear the sound of thudding hoofbeats, and, startled, she turned to observe the approach of Scott and Cheryl. As they drew rein she began to explain the cause of Danny's tears, but Cheryl cut her short.

'There's no need to go into details,' she said maliciously. 'We saw everything from the fenceline. We've been over there for ages, but you were too busy to notice us.'

Lindy's jaw dropped slightly as a feeling of horror gripped her. Did this mean they'd watched Steve kiss her? She looked at Scott but he merely returned her gaze in stony silence, his face cold, his mouth a grim line.

Cheryl said, 'We noticed you're not very good at taking care of small boys and their kites, but you're an expert at kissing their uncles.' Her shrill laugh echoed on the morning air.

Lindy felt herself go hot. She sent a further desperate look of appeal towards Scott, but there was no response or softening of his expression which was plainly one of condemnation. She could only presume he'd lost confidence in her, nor was the reason difficult to understand. She had assured him that she had not come to Whitecliffs because of Steve, yet it hadn't taken him long to discover her in his stepbrother's arms.

For several moments he continued to stare at her in silence, then, with a brief word to Cheryl, he wheeled his horse and rode away.

Cheryl sent a triumphant smile towards Lindy as she turned to follow him, her red hair flying in the wind.

CHAPTER FIVE

LINDY was conscious of a growing depression as she stood watching the two riders canter away from her, but her attention was soon claimed by Danny who gave a joyful shout.

'Uncle Steve has found my kite, he's found my kite.'

This was indeed true; Steve was now trudging across the field towards them, and he carried the red and yellow bird with its long tail streamers dragging behind him.

'It came down beyond the poplars,' he explained. 'Fortunately it's undamaged, although half its string is still caught up in the branches.' He looked at Danny. 'I'm afraid that's all for today, old chap.'

Danny nodded and accepted the situation. 'Can we look at the river instead?' he pleaded.

'I suppose so,' Steve agreed reluctantly. 'But don't imagine you're going near it, because it's a dangerous river in winter. It's swift and deep, and sometimes it rises beyond the willows to flood these flat areas.'

Danny's eyes became round. 'Does it get *angry* in winter?'

Steve laughed. 'It sure does. Storms in the mountains fill it up and give it a dirty muddy colour. Perhaps that makes it get mad. But by summer it has lost its rage and is down to being a nice polite stretch of water that allows us to walk along its banks.' His words came to an abrupt halt as though realising where Danny's thoughts could be led. His mother's last walk had been along that same bank.

They wandered to where the bare weeping willows grew near the water, their gnarled trunks leaning in disorderly array. Beyond them and across the river the high perpendicular limestone stretched in a long gradual bend.

It shone whitely in a brief flash of late morning sunshine, throwing into relief the small patches of scrubby growth that sprouted and clung from soil-filled clefts. In places the walls were deeply gouged where water from above had channelled its way through grooves down the cliff faces, and one gully, deeper than the rest, cut into it to form the dark twisted crevice which led down to the wide opening at the bottom.

Steve said, 'You can see where the place gets its name.'

'Yes, but I'd like to be seeing it in summer, rather than in winter.'

'Something tells me you'll be here in summer.' His voice was full of confidence.

She shook her head doubtfully. 'Something tells me I'll be here for only a month.'

A wet splash hit her face, and glancing up she realised the overhead clouds had darkened. 'It's going to rain, just as Ellie said. We must take Danny home. In any case it's nearly lunch time.'

They made their way back to the house, reaching it as the shower developed into a steady downpour. Lindy changed Danny's clothes to make sure he didn't catch a chill, then stepped from her own tracksuit into a heather-mixture jersey and skirt.

She then went to the kitchen to see if she could help Ellie, and at once realised that the small plump woman was in a disgruntled mood. She had little to say and her mouth had become buttoned into a tight line.

Disturbed, Lindy asked timidly, 'Have I offended you in some way, Ellie? Please tell me.'

'You? Of course not,' Ellie snapped. 'It's that other one. She makes me *mad*. She gets under my skin.' There was an angry silence until more words burst forth.

'Why on earth Steve had to bring her home to flaunt herself before Scott I'll never know.'

Lindy was now well aware of Steve's motive but she merely said, 'You don't like Cheryl, Ellie?'

'No, I don't. I know it's not my place to like or dislike visitors who come to this place, but it'll be a sad day if Scott is unwise enough to marry her. It'll also be the end of my job here, and Bert's.'

Lindy was puzzled by so much vehemence. 'Why, Ellie? Why do you dislike her so much?'

'Because she's a two-faced she-devil. She was supposed to have been Adrianne's friend, but I consider she merely used Adrianne to enable her to come here. Of course she was after Scott, she's been trying to catch him for years and I'm always afraid she'll succeed.'

'I wonder why Adrianne was so friendly with her,' Lindy mused.

'I used to wonder about it until my Bert put his finger right on the spot. Bert's more observant than one would imagine.'

Lindy, secretly amused, was nevertheless interested in Bert's opinion of the situation. 'What was Bert's diagnosis?' she asked.

Ellie lowered her voice. 'Well, Bert declared that Adrianne was like a pale lily. Oh yes, she was a nice kind person and we all loved her, but possibly because of her health she had very little real vitality in her. This seemed to make her lack in personality, and she knew it.'

'Are you saying her character was the opposite to Cheryl's?'

'In every way. When it suits her Cheryl can display a bright and vivid personality. She made a fuss of Adrianne, making the poor girl feel important. In fact Bert declared that Cheryl had Adrianne completely mesmerised, and when he said that I knew he'd hit the nail right on the head.'

Lindy smiled. 'I take it you don't want to see Scott mesmerised.'

'You can say that again—at least not by her.' Ellie drew a deep breath. 'Well, I feel better now I've got that lot off my chest. Tell me, where are they?'

Lindy looked at the rain trickling down the window-pane. 'I don't know, somewhere out there. Perhaps they're sheltering in a barn or in the woolshed,' she added dolefully. Sighing, she realised that Cheryl, with Scott to herself, would be making the most of her opportunities.

Ellie looked at her despondent face. 'Oh, so it's like that, is it? I'm not surprised.'

Lindy looked at her quickly. 'Like—like what?'

'It hasn't taken you long to appreciate Scott's qualities. Now be honest and admit that's the truth.'

'My dear Ellie, I've known him for only a couple of days,' she protested, snatching at her dignity.

Ellie shrugged. 'So what? Sometimes love can come quickly. It can bring a person down like a shot duck.'

The subject was not one that Lindy wished to pursue and she was more than grateful when Danny came into the kitchen declaring himself to be hungry.

Ellie cut a slice of pie that stood waiting to be served, and the small boy ate it with relish.

Steve then entered the kitchen, closely followed by Bert, and the conversation became general with a description of the kite-flying. Bert had just declared that he knew where a large ball of string could be found when the back door opened to admit Scott and Cheryl, both in an extremely damp state.

Cheryl's wet bedraggled hair could no longer be described as a flaming cloud, while her face was marred with unsightly blotches and streaks of black mascara.

The sight of it brought loud uncontrolled giggles from Danny. 'You look funny,' he told her with embarrassing candour. Then, almost choking on his mirth, 'Doesn't she look funny, Lindy?'

Cheryl drew in a sharp breath. 'What's he talking about?' she demanded, looking suspiciously at the grinning faces of the men.

Lindy felt a surge of sympathy for her. She moved closer and whispered urgently. 'Go and wash your face.'

Cheryl flashed her a look of momentary anger, then her colour rose as she hastily left the room, her exit being followed by low chuckles from Steve and Bert.

By the time she rejoined them they were drinking pre-lunch sherries in the lounge. Renewed make-up and a change into her flamboyant dress of brilliant green had restored her confidence, and with the divine right of a queen she took her place beside Scott, resting on a stool at his feet and leaning against his leg.

Lindy watched her efforts to monopolise him, and when they went to the dining-room it seemed clear she was determined to act as his hostess. At first she felt only tolerant amusement, but as Cheryl's condescending attitude towards herself became more apparent she knew a sense of growing irritation. Nor did this abate after lunch when they relaxed in the lounge to watch a Sunday afternoon TV movie.

'We can all sit on this nice long settee,' Cheryl said with an air of authority. 'Lindy and I will sit in the middle, with you two men at the ends.'

'Good idea,' Steve agreed. He pushed the settee into position, then drew Lindy down to sit beside him.

His action played nicely into Cheryl's plans, and moments later she was sitting close to Scott, her satisfaction evident as she turned to gaze at his face.

The film, like so many of the Sunday afternoon movies, was the repeat of an old one. Lindy had seen it before and she soon lost interest. From the corner of her eye she could see Cheryl continually turning to gaze at Scott's profile, and she could also feel Steve sliding his arm from the back of the settee to rest it about her shoulders. His fingers fondled her neck and stroked her cheek.

'*Stop it*,' she hissed at him.

He laughed easily and removed his hand, but a short time later she felt his fingers tracing the curve of her ear. She bore it in silence until her patience snapped and she again whispered angrily, 'Steve, will you please stop.'

Cheryl turned to look at her. 'What's the matter? Won't Steve keep his hands to himself? I don't blame him, after the encouragement you gave him down on the riverflats.' Her words ended on a low laugh.

Lindy looked beyond Cheryl to find Scott regarding her, his eyes bleak with accusation. She bit her lip, turned away and made an effort to concentrate on the film, but this proved to be an impossibility.

A short time later the feel of Steve's fingers again gently stroking her neck sent a surge of irritation coursing through her. She stood up abruptly and said, 'Actually, I've seen this film before, so if you'll excuse me I'd like to take the Correspondence School envelopes up to the tower and examine them.'

'Surely you've examined them before now,' Cheryl mocked.

'Only briefly. I've given them little more than several quick glances, therefore I'd like to go over them more thoroughly before I begin with Danny in the morning.'

'Take Steve with you,' Cheryl suggested. 'I'm sure he'd be a great help in sorting out primer one work.' She laughed as if the thought struck her as being extremely funny.

'Yes, sure, I'll come too.' Steve made a move to rise to his feet. 'I reckon I could give advice.'

'No, thank you,' Lindy protested hastily. 'I'd prefer to study them alone.' She was well aware that Cheryl was grasping at the opportunity to be alone with Scott.

The slight agitation in her voice appeared to have registered with him. He swept a penetrating glance over her, then said in clipped tones, 'How about leaving Lindy to do as she wishes?'

'Yes, please, I'd be glad if you'd do just that,' she said, glancing from Cheryl to Steve. Then, looking at Scott's hard expression she became aware of a sinking feeling that told her he couldn't care less whether she remained with them or not. And as if to echo this sentiment the sound of laughter and music from the film followed her along the passage.

In the privacy of her room she subjected herself to a long and critical scrutiny in the mirror. Her spirits slumped as she decided that the face staring back at her could not possibly compete with Cheryl's special kind of beauty, but there was little she could do about it.

Then, taking herself to task, she realised that Cheryl, in her own subtle manner, was beginning to give her an inferiority complex, and, squaring her shoulders with sudden determination, she resolved she would not allow this to happen. She had a job to do and she'd get on with it, although not for one moment did she believe it would last beyond the one month's trial.

The polythene bag she carried upstairs weighed heavily with Correspondence School work and the extra books she herself had purchased. But when she reached the tower she discovered she would not be alone, as Danny was already there, accompanied, as usual, by his teddy.

The small boy sat on the floor beside a box of plastic animals and parts of buildings he was busily fitting together. 'I'm making my farm,' he informed her as he clicked white rails into place. 'This is the fence that goes right round everything. Uncle Scott says it's the boundary.'

Kneeling beside him she was unable to resist an impulsive kiss on his soft round cheek before examining the sheep, cows and horses. Each animal was perfect in detail and able to stand firmly on its tiny hoofs. 'Do you know how many animals you have, Danny? I don't expect you can count yet.'

He was indignant. 'Course I can count. Right up to ten. Ellie taught me to say one, two, the cow says moo, three, four, the bull will roar, five, six, the donkey kicks, seven, eight, shut the gate, nine, ten, the dog's name's Ben.'

'Very good,' she applauded, peering into the box to find further farmyard pieces in the form of pigs, hens, dogs and even a cat with its kittens. 'You seem to have everything,' she commented.

'Uncle Scott found them all for me,' he said simply. 'Sometimes he lets me put my hand in his pocket and then I'll find a new one.'

Scott's voice spoke from the doorway. 'I'm still looking for deer. I'd like to find him a couple of stags and a few hinds.'

'It's a beautiful set,' she said quietly, being unsure of what to say and wondering why he had come up to the tower. Surely it wasn't in search of her? 'Is the film finished?' she asked after several moments of thought.

'No. I became bored with it.'

'Even with such pleasant company?' It was an effort to keep her voice normal.

He ignored the question and said, 'I became curious about the Correspondence School work.' He moved to the table and began to examine the contents of the polythene bag. 'Where on earth do you begin? Perhaps you could sit beside me and pretend I'm Danny.' He drew the two chairs closer together.

'Then Lindy will have to kiss you like she kissed me,' Danny said unexpectedly from the floor.

'I suspect that would be beyond her,' Scott told him drily. 'Now if it had been Uncle Steve sitting here——' The dark grey eyes held a taunting expression.

pens. 'These were provided by the School?'

'No. They were my own idea. Danny will use them to trace over the letters to help with his printing.'

He sat back in his chair to regard her with a long scrutiny. 'I must say I'm impressed. You've taken this project very seriously.'

'Of course. How else would you expect me to take it? It's very important for Danny. It's part of his grounding.'

'I agree, but I had no idea there was so much to it. To be honest I hadn't given it much thought.' He raised a hand to stroke her cheek. 'Do you put as much depth into everything you do?'

His touch brought a flush to her cheeks. 'If it's important.'

'Which means you would also love deeply.' His eyes rested upon her lips, their inspection of their sweet softness bringing an even deeper colour to her face.

'Yes, I suppose so.' She was finding it impossible to meet his eyes.

'Steve could be a lucky man.'

Her eyes flashed. 'Look, would it be possible to get one thing straight?' But before she could finish her request there was a sound of steps on the stairs and then Cheryl entered the room.

Her glance swept over the pile of books. 'What on earth is all this? Ah, pardon me, the Correspondence School to be sure. Do you really imagine it's necessary?' she scoffed with a light laugh.

'It is to me,' Lindy replied quietly. 'And I think to Danny.'

'Well, it wouldn't be to *me*. But then, I'm *trained*, remember? Scott darling, how long to do you intend allowing her to fiddle about with all this—*this stuff*? Surely you're not wasting a whole *month* on it?'

'A month is what I said, Cheryl. Did you have a special reason for coming up here?'

'Oh, yes, Ellie's made tea. It's in the lounge, if *teacher* will allow you out of the schoolroom.'

The words spoken jokingly held a barb. Then, as though fearing she might be nearing the edge of Scott's tolerance, she took Lindy's arm with a show of friendliness. 'Come along, you must be *dying* for a cup of tea.'

'Ted's coming too,' Danny exclaimed, snatching up the bear and racing ahead of them.

Steve was watching the end of the film when they reached the lounge. His eyes remained glued to the screen, and it took Lindy only a few minutes to detect a definite coolness in his attitude towards her. She was puzzled, but decided to ignore it, and not until later did she learn the reason for his fit of pique.

The opportunity for her to do so came when she decided to write letters in the privacy of the bedroom. Sitting in the chair with the pad on her knee she had just sealed and addressed an envelope to her mother, and was about to begin a letter to Judith, when she looked up to discover Steve scowling at her from the doorway. His entry startled her.

'It didn't take long for Scott to follow you up to the tower,' he said belligerently.

She looked at him in surprise. 'Is that so? I really didn't notice. He came up to examine the Correspondence School work.'

'Oh yeah? No doubt that was his excuse.'

'You've got to be joking if you imagine he needed an excuse to enter any room of his own house.'

'I'm not joking. What I'm saying is that I didn't arrange for you to come here for his benefit.'

She regarded him steadily. 'I know exactly why I'm here, Steve. Lessons begin in the morning and it's only natural for Scott to take an interest in them.'

'Huh! He's interested in more than the lessons, and you know it,' he snarled. 'I suppose you've been giving him the come-hither look with those sparkly eyes of yours.'

She flushed, feeling indignant by the suggestion that she should deliberately ogle Scott, then, controlling her annoyance, she forced herself to laugh. 'A lot of use that would be with Cheryl sitting beside him.'

'Cheryl's pretty enough if a man's mad on redheads, but when it comes to quality, he'll sure recognise it in you.' His eyes narrowed. 'Has he made a pass at you?'

'You must be dreaming,' she retorted, flushing again as she recalled previous moments in the tower. Nevertheless her spirits rose. Had Scott been interested in more than the lessons? Would he leave Cheryl's side to come to hers? She doubted it, although the thought brought a more hopeful expression to her face, and it was probably the slight smile on her lips that encouraged Steve to draw her to her feet and take her in his arms.

She was about to push him away with a firm shove, but then instinct warned her to take matters slowly, otherwise there could be open antagonism between them. This was something she wished to avoid, because, apart from affecting her concentration with Danny, it could also make her period at Whitecliffs unpleasant.

He said, 'Just remember, Lindy, while you're in this house you're my partner.'

She was startled. 'Partner? What are you talking about?'

'You know what I mean.' His expression had become belligerent.

'You're mistaken, Steve. I'm nobody's partner because I'm a free agent and intend to remain that way.' There was a pause while she closed her eyes and leaned against him wearily. How could she make him realise she looked upon him as a friend and nothing else?

Pondering the question she opened her eyes and was

shocked to meet a steely grey gaze from the doorway
where Scott stood watching them.

'A most touching scene,' he commented with an edge
to his voice. 'I'd hate to disturb the——er——proceedings.'
And with that terse remark he disappeared along the
passage and into his room.

As she heard his bedroom door slam she realised it
was the second time Scott had observed her in Steve's
arms, and the knowledge irritated her almost beyond
endurance. Wrenching herself from the embrace she
hissed furiously, 'Now get this straight, Steve Langley, I
am *not* your property, and if you pester me in any way
at all I'll leave this place right smartly. Get it?'

Taken aback he stared at her in amazement. 'Sure, I
get it. My God, you're a little spitfire. Scott's welcome
to you, if that's what you've got in mind, and if you can
prise him away from Cheryl.' And with a show of self-
righteous indignation he strode from the room.

At that moment all hope of avoiding open warfare
with Steve appeared to have evaporated, but by next
morning he was his usual friendly self and seemed to
have forgotten the incident. But some of his words
remained in Lindy's mind. Had Scott come up to the
tower in search of her company, or merely to look at
the Correspondence School lessons?

Hopes that he could possibly wish to seek her
company were dashed after breakfast when she stood at
the kitchen window to watch Scott and Cheryl ride
away. The heavy rain had ceased overnight, and
although Cheryl was wrapped against the chilly wind
sweeping down from the snow-clad ranges she still
managed to look like a model from a magazine cover.

Ellie came to stand beside her. 'Don't let her worry
you,' she consoled. 'She'll be away next weekend. You
just put your mind to the boy's lessons and the time will
slip by quickly.'

'Her presence doesn't worry me, Ellie,' Lindy said in

an effort to reassure herself, yet knowing the words to be untrue. And in that moment she gave up trying to fool herself because, despite the short time she'd known him, she felt strangely drawn to Scott. When he spoke his deep voice seemed to sing in her ears and she was also conscious that his vibrant masculinity had awakened new emotions within herself.

But thank heaven she had something else to think about, and shaking herself mentally she dragged her eyes from the disappearing riders. It was an effort to push Scott's image from her mind but she said firmly, 'Come along Danny, it's time for school.'

Ellie gave the little boy a hug. 'This is a special day for you, darling. It's your first day with a teacher. Now you listen carefully to everything.' She turned to Lindy. 'Where will you begin?'

'By making a hat out of brown paper,' Lindy smiled. 'After that we'll talk about why we wear hats and the different kinds of hats we wear in summer or on rainy days. And when we know all about hats we'll read about the hat that was blown away by the wind.'

'*Hats*! Good gracious!'

'After about fifteen minutes we'll change to a colouring-in book and crayons so that he doesn't have too long on any one subject.'

'Come down for a break soon after ten,' Ellie advised as they left the room. 'The scones will be out of the oven and morning tea will be on the table. Some of the others will be in,' she added significantly, her face holding an expression that was full of meaning.

Lindy smiled to herself as she went up the stairs. She's been at Whitecliffs for such a short time, yet already Ellie was coupling her with Scott. Didn't Ellie realise it was hopeless to do so? Couldn't she see the attention he was paying Cheryl?

She brushed the thoughts from her mind as she reached the tower and began to settle down to work with Danny. Nor was it long before she discovered he was an interested pupil with a string of questions simmering in his mind. However, there were a few distractions. If a dog barked he rushed to the window to discover who was in the field below, and if voices were heard he fled downstairs to see who had arrived. She smiled to herself, knowing that his avid curiosity would later encourage him to seek knowledge.

Later, when she went downstairs for morning tea, the kitchen seemed to be full of people. Bert and Steve were there with Jake Lomas, the deer manager. Scott and Cheryl had returned from wherever they had been riding, but Lindy hardly saw the others because her attention was caught by the radiance on Cheryl's face.

Her heart sank as she guessed there must be a reason for it, but although she sent Scott a searching glance his inscrutable expression told her nothing. He merely sipped his tea and held a quiet discussion with Jake Lomas.

But Ellie, it seemed, had also noticed the gleam of satisfaction in Cheryl's eyes. 'You're looking quite lovely today, Cheryl,' she said kindly. 'You must be very happy about something.'

Cheryl glowed. 'Oh yes, I am. Scott's so *kind* to me.'

'He's kind to everyone,' Ellie reminded her.

Cheryl's smile widened. 'Yes, I *know*, but to *me* he's always so—so *marvellous*.' Her wide gaze turned to Scott.

He shifted uncomfortably, then gave a short laugh. 'You can cut out your blarney, Cheryl'

Danny then claimed his attention. The small boy had rushed upstairs and had returned with a page of hats he'd been colouring. He also wore his paper hat. Pointing to the page he said, 'Look, Uncle Scott, that's the farmer's old brown hat that blows away.'

Steve, however, was not to be side-tracked by Danny and his crayon work. Obviously interested in Cheryl's elated state he said slyly, 'Could it be that you and

Scott have something of importance to tell us, perhaps an announcement of some sort?' he added delicately.

Lindy knew he referred to an engagement. She watched Cheryl's cheeks flame, then began a silent but desperate prayer within herself. *Oh no, no, please don't let it be that. Don't let them become engaged unless— unless she's the right person for Scott, someone who'll make him happy*. And in that moment she realised the depth of her own feelings for him, and the staggering fact that she herself had fallen in love with him.

The blinding knowledge hit her suddenly, striking with full force like a meteor hurtling from outer space, and she knew that this was something she would have to face up to. She felt shaken and completely dazed as she moved to the window to stare unseeingly at the leafless fruit trees in the orchard beyond the vegetable garden.

Nor was this overpowering sensation like anything she'd ever experienced before, and even as she struggled to grapple with the shock of her newly discovered love the voices behind her rose and fell in a mass of jumbled sound until Steve's voice cut clearly above the rest.

'Come clean, Cheryl,' he said. 'Anyone can see you're sailing along on cloud nine. If it's not an engagement, what, exactly, has sent you up into the air?'

'I don't have to go home at the end of the week,' she told him happily. 'Scott has invited me to stay for another week, and if he hadn't *wanted* me to stay he wouldn't have *asked* me, now would he?'

Lindy's spirits plummeted at the news. She turned to look at Ellie and noticed her mouth had become gripped in a thin line of disapproval. And then she caught the quick glance of satisfaction Steve had flicked towards herself. It only added to her depression, and now, with the state of her own emotions laid bare before her eyes, she wondered how she would cope with the situation.

CHAPTER SIX

CHERYL's voice, slightly high-pitched with gratification, grated on Lindy's ears. 'It's so *sweet* of Scott to *want* me to stay. It's really to help me become used to the fact that our—our dear Adrianne is no longer here.'

'Shut up, Cheryl,' Scott snapped unexpectedly. 'That's a subject we don't enlarge upon in front of a certain party.' He frowned at her then glanced at Danny.

Cheryl looked startled. 'Oh, I see. Well, you know what I mean. It's just that I'm so *grateful*.'

'Yes, yes, we know all about that.' His tone was still abrupt.

Jake Lomas then came to the rescue by changing the subject to matters concerning the next deer sale to be held on the property. Parking arrangements for trucks were discussed, as well as the number of weaner hinds ready to be sold. The latter, Lindy soon realised, were the fawns that had recently left their mothers.

In the midst of the discussion Lindy took Danny upstairs to resume lessons, but when she reached the tower the turmoil raging within her mind made concentration almost impossible until Danny looked up at her, his blue eyes full of appeal.

'Can we have a story now?' he pleaded.

'Yes, of course,' she agreed almost eagerly. 'We'll have Goldilocks and the Three Bears.'

'Goody-goody, Ted likes to hear about bears.'

When the story was finished she drew a sheet of white paper towards her. 'I'll print a letter and you will trace over it until you can copy it. This is letter A, and this is letter B. B stands for Bear.' She pointed to it on the page.

The printing session was in progress when Scott came into the room, his unexpected appearance making her catch her breath and sending the blood rushing to her face.

He looked at Danny's efforts and was impressed. 'For a first morning you appear to have achieved wonders.'

She shook her head. 'Don't applaud me, I'm simply following the Correspondence School method. They are the people who achieve wonders so long as the pupil has someone to guide him through the various exercises.' Then, before she could control her tongue she added, 'You're without your shadow.'

He frowned. 'What do you mean?'

'Cheryl, of course. She's hardly left your side.'

'Your imagination does you credit.' He paused, then admitted, 'Actually she was coming up here with me when Ellie asked for her assistance in some small task.'

'Ellie asked for her help?' Lindy's tone betrayed her amazement.

'I must say I was surprised, but perhaps Ellie's attitude towards Cheryl is softening.'

'And you'd like to see that happen?'

'It matters not, one way or the other.'

Lindy smiled to herself. Dear Ellie, she'd waylaid Cheryl to enable Scott to come up alone.

He said, 'Anyhow, what about your own shadow?'

'I haven't one,' she assured him calmly.

'Huh! You could've fooled me. Isn't it time you admitted that my first suspicions concerning yourself and Steve are correct?'

'Certainly not. Steve and I will never be more than just good friends. He's well aware of that fact.'

'I have a strong conviction his aspirations go beyond mere friendship, in fact a long way beyond.'

'His aspirations?' she cut in. 'What about my feelings in the matter? Haven't I any say at all?' she flashed angrily. 'You men make me tired. You imagine a girl's just sitting round waiting to be gathered up, or replaced on the shelf just as it suits you.'

He gave a sudden laugh. '*You*—on the shelf? That's really funny.'

'It's not at all funny,' she told him seriously. 'If I find myself loving a man who—who does not love me, it's more than likely I'll remain unmarried.'

'Steve would never allow such a tragedy.'

She drew a deep breath then hissed furiously, 'For heaven's sake, how can I convince you?'

'Perhaps it would be better if I try to judge for myself.' He gazed down into her eyes for several moments, then turned to Danny. 'Lessons are over for this morning, old chap. Run down and show Ellie all this good printing you've been doing. You can stay with her until lunch is ready.'

And as Danny disappeared he took Lindy in his arms.

Taken by surprise she was momentarily startled, and while a sudden fear warned she was in danger of betraying her love for him, common sense urged her to grasp every precious second with both hands. She was in Scott's arms and it might never happen again. The joy of feeling his lips trace a line across her brow sent a surge of excitement coursing through her blood, and as his arms moulded her against his body she yielded to their pressure with a small sigh of contentment.

'You know you're a witch,' he accused quietly, his lips gently brushing her petal-soft cheek while finding their way to her throat.

Her heart thudded, and every nerve tingled as the tip of his tongue teased a wildly beating pulse. She waited for his lips to find hers, again warning herself against a response that would tell him of the longing ache that raged within, and now held her in a grip she feared would never let go.

But when the moment came she was helpless and unable to keep her longing for him hidden. Her arms clung to him as she responded with abandon to the bruising force of his kiss. The turmoil of his passion made itself evident as he crushed her to him, and with a shock she realised his hunger was as consuming as her own. But was it hunger for her love? No, it was merely hunger for her body—or so she told herself.

At last, sighing as the realisation of this fact began to spread its roots in her mind, she drew her mouth from his and leaned her head against his shoulder. She could hear his heart thudding in time with her own racing pulses, and she was well aware that one hand held her breast. She also knew she should remove it, but instead she savoured the joy of feeling his touch.

His voice came from above her head. 'I believe you,' he said.

She was at a loss to understand his meaning. 'You—what?'

'I believe you're free of any love you might have had for Steve. Whatever you felt for him previously, it's gone.'

'Oh, yes, I'd forgotten you were just putting me to the test.' What an idiot she was to have allowed herself to be carried away.

'Test?' He looked at her in a dazed manner.

'You were supposed to be "judging for yourself," remember?'

Gently, she tried to free herself from his arms, but found herself still held in the firm grip that clasped her to him. His lips found hers again, but before many moments had passed a slight sound caught their ears.

Imperceptible as it was it made them draw apart and turn to meet the wide blue eyes of Danny as he peeped at them round the half-open door. His slightly sagging jaw made it all too obvious that their embrace had been fully observed.

'I told you to stay downstairs,' Scott rasped.

Danny vanished with a clatter of small feet on the stairs, and then his voice floated up to them as he shouted for all to hear, *'Uncle Scott's kissing Lindy, Uncle Scott's kissing Lindy.'*

'Damn!' The angry exclamation escaped Scott as he strode from the room.

Lindy heard him pound down the stairs and within seconds the sound of a door bang floated up to her. It sent her to peer through the windows, and moments later she saw him leading the grey mare and his own black gelding towards the horse paddock which lay a short distance from the house.

The sudden plunging from heaven to earth had thrown her into a shaken state, and although lunch was a distance from being ready she knew she would have to go downstairs eventually. But in the meantime she was reluctant to leave the tower.

In fact she was almost afraid to go downstairs, because Cheryl would most certainly have heard Danny's shouted information. She would know that Scott had kissed her, and, conscious of a sudden tension, Lindy wondered what the reaction would be.

The answer to this question was not long in arriving. Rapid steps sounded on the stairs, the door was flung open and Cheryl stepped into the room. She then closed the door behind her and stood leaning with her back against it while she surveyed Lindy through narrowed lids.

'I believe you have ideas of stepping in on my territory,' she said coldly.

Lindy was reminded of a lioness defending its lair, but she remained calm. 'What exactly is your territory, Cheryl?'

'Scott, of course, as you no doubt realise. Unless you're very, *very* dumb you must be able to see we're almost engaged.'

'When I see you wearing his ring I'll wish you every

happiness,' Lindy said. She forced herself to smile although the thought twisted her heart.

'It won't be long.' Cheryl's voice rang with confidence. 'In the meantime I don't want interference from a young city upstart who has come here under false pretences. Schoolteacher indeed, huh,' she sneered.

There was something so childish about Cheryl's vehemence that Lindy was forced to giggle, and as mirth took hold of her Cheryl looked at her with suspicion.

'I suppose Scott *did* kiss you? The little brat of a boy isn't just telling fibs?'

Lindy's face became wreathed in smiles. 'Oh no, Danny's not lying, and Scott *did* kiss me. It was— *wonderful*,' she added simply, unaware of the joy shining from her eyes.

The significance of her radiant face was not lost upon Cheryl. Her mouth twisted as she said, 'I'm warning you, you just watch it, Lindy Farrell.'

Lindy's eyes widened as she looked at her steadily. '*Watch it?* What are you talking about?'

'You'll keep your eyes off Scott,' Cheryl gritted from behind clenched teeth. 'I've waited for him for years and I don't intend to allow an ambitious little nobody to step in.'

'Aren't you forgetting something, Cheryl?'

'What do you mean?'

'Don't you know that all's fair in love and war?'

Cheryl drew herself to her full height, her green eyes flashing angrily as they glared at Lindy. 'Are you saying you'll *fight* me for *my man*?'

'I didn't actually say that,' Lindy protested.

'It's what you implied. And what about Steve? He looked stricken when Danny came rushing downstairs. The poor man had just come in from a cold wintry day to be greeted by the news that he was being double-crossed.'

The words brought a laugh from Lindy. 'What utter rubbish. You're well aware he's been inside for ages, drinking tea beside the fire. And apart from that, you're exaggerating. Steve knows only too well that we're just good friends. There is nothing—absolutely *nothing*—of a serious nature between us,' she added crisply.

Suddenly she felt she'd had enough of Cheryl. She also knew that sooner or later she must go downstairs to face further reaction aroused by Danny's news of what he'd seen. But in the meantime she could delay the moment by preparing work for him to do. Lines for his printing were to be ruled on blank paper; therefore ignoring Cheryl she busied herself with this task.

Later, when she peeped into the kitchen, Ellie greeted her with a pleased smile, while Bert grinned, winked, and said nothing. It was his way of indicating his approval.

She then went into the lounge where she found Steve and Scott. Steve's mouth was set and she wondered if angry words had passed between them, nor was she surprised when he ignored her by getting up and leaving the room.

Scott offered her a sherry. His grey eyes were sombre as he looked down into her face. 'You'd better drink this. I'm afraid you're about to face the music.'

She looked at him gravely. 'The war drums have already started beating. I'm sure you know what I mean.'

'Are you saying someone has already had words with you?'

'A few. I've been given the message.'

'Cheryl, I presume? Where is she?'

'I believe she went to her room. Would it help if I assured her that—that it meant nothing?'

'You're referring to those moments in the tower?'

'Of course, what else?' Her eyes, looking up into his, held a pathetic question within their depths.

'Are you saying they meant nothing to you?' His eyes

had become penetrating in their scrutiny of her face.

She found herself unable to reply. Instead she stared at the pale gold liquid in her glass, then sipped her sherry.

'At least they meant something to me.' The light nonchalance in his voice hit her ears.

She looked at him wonderingly. 'They did?'

'Yes. They convinced me that you're not in love with Steve. As you said, there's only friendship between you, at least on your part. Not that he's keen to accept the fact.'

'I'm glad you realise it,' she said in a low voice.

'I don't believe you'd have responded to me as you did, if you'd had any love for Steve.'

She felt herself go cold. 'Are you saying you were just putting me to the—the test?'

'There are times when we're all put to the test,' he informed her cynically.

'I see.' She drained her glass then put it down shakily. 'Well, that should be a comfort to Cheryl.'

At that moment Ellie came into the room. 'Lunch is on the dining-room table,' she told them cheerfully. 'Steve's there already, but I can't persuade Cheryl to come out of her bedroom. I told her she's making too much fuss over a trifling matter.'

'What exactly did you say to her, Ellie?' Scott asked.

'I told her I knew why she was upset and that you'd probably given Lindy a small peck on the cheek in gratitude for the effort she's making with Danny, and that it didn't mean a thing.'

'How right you are, Ellie,' Lindy put in quickly. 'It doesn't mean a thing to either of us.' This was only a half-truth because to her it had meant a great deal, but, with her chin raised, she snatched at the opportunity to save her pride.

'Perhaps I'd better speak to her,' Scott said. 'I do not intend to have an unpleasant atmosphere in this house.'

'Everything will be all right when you explain about the *test*,' Lindy told him with forced sweetness.

He sent her a long searching look, then left the room to stride along the passage.

'What do you mean by a *test*?' Ellie whispered, her eyes full of curiosity. 'No; I've no right to ask.'

Lindy shook her head. 'I—I'm afraid I can't explain.' She turned away to stare through the window.

'I suppose that kiss *was* just a peck on the cheek as I suggested?'

A flush rose to Lindy's cheeks as the memory of it brought a smile to her lips. 'No, it couldn't be put into that category at all.' Nor was it possible for her to meet Ellie's eyes.

'A real kiss, was it? I must say that's interesting, very interesting indeed.' The brown eyes were alert.

Lindy turned to look at her. 'Oh? What's so interesting about it? After all, it was only a kiss.'

'Because Scott isn't the type who kisses all and sundry. Those two men were always very different in that respect. Steve, for instance, had girlfriends posted in various places while Scott didn't run after them at all.'

'Are you saying he's a woman-hater?'

'Not at all,' Ellie hastened to assure her. 'Thinking of the situation I believe Steve hasn't married because he has too many girlfriends, and Scott's not married because he's too discerning. He hasn't met the right one. Now please go and have your lunch.'

When Lindy entered the dining-room she found the others were about to begin with soup before cutting into one of Ellie's tasty pizzas. Cheryl, she noticed, had renewed her make-up and was being deliberately cheerful although she managed to ignore Lindy in a subtle manner as she chatted to Steve and Scott.

Steve answered her in monosyllables and appeared to be morose. He also ignored Lindy, and after finishing his meal he muttered something about getting back to Jake Lomas and the new deer fence. He then pushed back his chair and left the table, striding from the room without looking at anybody.

Cheryl watched his departure. 'I feel so *sorry* for him, he's *very* upset.' The baleful glance she sent Lindy was loaded with accusation.

'He'll recover,' Scott commented drily. 'He's been given a dose of his own medicine and he's not keen on the taste.'

Cheryl sighed, then sent Scott a bewitching glance as she changed the subject. 'Well, what are we doing this afternoon?'

He gave a slight shrug. 'You may come to the woolshed with me if you wish. The crutchers will be there.'

'If I *wish*? Of *course* I wish.' A smile played about her lips as she slid a small gloating smile towards Lindy.

During the meal Lindy had found difficulty in meeting Scott's eyes. A sense of shyness had gripped her, while memory of the excitement she'd felt when being held in his arms caused a vague unease to develop in her mind. The reason for this was her own ardent response, and the more she recalled the uninhibited display of joy and rapture with which she'd clung to him, the more she feared he must guess that her feelings towards him were not merely casual.

She was also disturbed by the sombre expression in Scott's grey eyes when they happened to rest upon her during the meal. It was almost as though they held a warning that she'd be wise to watch her step, that she must understand she'd be heading for heartbreak if she were unwise enough to set her sights on any serious alliance between them.

Nor did she pause to consider whether or not these fears were little more than her imagination, therefore as soon as she was reasonably able to do so, she rose from the table, stacked the dishes on to the trolley and pushed it out to the kitchen.

A short time later she again stood with Ellie to watch Cheryl and Scott ride away from the house. 'Where are they going?' Ellie asked as she peered through the window above the kitchen sink.

'To the woolshed,' Lindy told her dismally. 'Scott said something about crutchers. I'm abysmally ignorant about farming matters. What are crutchers?'

Ellie sent her an amused glance. 'They're shearers, really. They'll clean up the back ends of every sheep on the place. When the grass becomes soft the sheep are inclined to scour, the droppings cling to the wool and have to be removed.' She gave a derisive laugh. 'A most romantic experience for Cheryl, I *don't* think. She won't even be able to hear herself speak above the din of the shearing machines.'

'She won't mind,' Lindy said with understanding. 'She'll be with Scott, which is her main ambition.' She sighed inwardly, knowing that she herself would not object to the noise and smells of the woolshed if it meant being there with Scott Wardell.

Ellie said, 'I can't understand him. Really, I can't understand him at all.' Her tone rang with impatience.

'What do you mean?'

'All this attention he's been dancing on Cheryl. He's never done it before, so why start now?'

'Perhaps it's because she was Adrianne's friend. Perhaps she seems to bring Adrianne back in some strange way.'

Ellie shook her head. 'In that case he could've invited her here ages ago, but has he done so? No. And don't forget it wasn't Scott who invited her here this time, yet it seems as though he's grasping at her company. I tell you, he's got me puzzled.'

Depression descended upon Lindy as the situation took on the clarity of a blinding light. 'I'm not even remotely puzzled,' she said. 'I think Scott fell in love with Cheryl some years ago, but at the time she wasn't ready for marriage. At that time she found Whitecliffs to be too remote, too isolated.'

'And now she's changed her mind, do you think?'

'Very definitely. She's older now and ready to settle down.' She gave Ellie a graphic description of the scene with Cheryl in the tower.

The older woman's eyes widened with surprise. 'My goodness, no wonder she bit my head off when I told her lunch was ready.' She paused thoughtfully, then asked, 'So how do you think he's taking this change in her attitude?'

'It seems quite obvious to me,' Lindy said sadly. 'He's seeking her company in an effort to decide whether or not he's in love with her. He's just making *sure*.'

'That sort of indecision doesn't sound like the Scott Wardell I've known for many years,' Ellie declared flatly. 'And there's another thing, isn't it Cheryl who is seeking *his* company, rather than the other way round? Besides, it doesn't give him a reason for kissing *you*.'

'Perhaps he imagined I was Cheryl,' Lindy said dolefully.

'Rubbish, absolute stuff and nonsense,' Ellie snapped crossly.

Lindy decided it was time to change the subject. 'Where's Danny?' she asked, recalling her duties towards that small person.

Ellie laughed. 'He's up in the tower room waiting for teacher. Today the new broom sweeps clean, but I can't guarantee he'll always be as keen about his lessons.'

When Lindy reached the tower she found Danny busy with felt-tip pens. The various colours from the box lay scattered across the table while he experimented with each one, scrawling circles and whirls over white art paper meant for use in his printing lessons.

'I'm drawing,' he told her proudly, starting on a new sheet.

'So you are,' she exclaimed, dismayed by the number of wasted pages. 'In future you'll draw only on the blackboard with chalk, and this paper must be kept for writing. Do you understand?'

He nodded.

'Right. Now we'll learn to print letter B.' Opening one of the Correspondence School books she followed the instructions by point-to words under pictures. 'There it is: b for bear, b for boy, b for baby.' She then drew a large b and, taking his hand, she guided his finger over it. As she did so she said, 'Down, halfway up the same line, round and join. There now, see if you can do it.'

After a few finger tracings he examined the array of felt-tip pens still lying on the table. His choice of a greyish yellow one was careful. 'What's the name of this colour?' he asked, his blue eyes serious as he looked up at her.

'It's called yellow ochre. Why do you choose that one?'

''Cos it's the same colour as Ted,' he explained simply.

A wave of affection for him engulfed her. No doubt he'd grow out of his adoration of his teddy, but in the meantime heaven help the household if anything happened to Ted. Danny would be heartbroken.

Lessons continued smoothly for the rest of the day, the concentration with Danny playing a large part in keeping Scott's face from hovering before her mind. However, she knew when he returned because Cheryl's gay laughter echoed through the house. Cheryl, it seemed, was in a happy mood, and it was only when Danny showed his drawings to Scott that her good temper vanished.

They were having their pre-dinner drinks in the

lounge when it happened. The small boy came into the room carrying a bundle of papers, and as he carefully spread the scribble-covered pages on the floor he said proudly, 'Look, Uncle Scott, I did these drawings today.'

Scott's brows rose as he surveyed the pages. His eyes questioned Lindy but he made no comment.

Steve, who was lounging in a chair, gave a short laugh. 'Ah, a budding abstract artist. Perhaps Lindy could guide him towards the steps of Picasso. He'll make a million and we'll all be kept in the luxury to which we aspire.'

She smiled dutifully at his feeble joke, realising that a couple of glasses of Scotch had eradicated the black mood prevailing at lunch time. But just as she was feeling relieved about this fact Cheryl turned upon her.

The green eyes flashed with a show of indignation as she lashed at Lindy. 'So, this is how you allow the child to waste time, to say nothing of wasting expensive art paper. Are you so stupid you don't know the value of such paper?'

Embarrassment made Lindy feel sick as she turned to Scott. 'I'm sorry, it was done before I returned to the tower after lunch. He thought he was doing so well.'

'Don't you know you have to watch him all the time? All children have to be continually watched,' Cheryl persisted scathingly.

'Shut up, Cheryl,' Scott snapped. 'You're making it sound like the end of the world.'

Cheryl's full lips became sulky. 'Okay, so long as you can see her—her utter *incompetence*,' she retorted viciously.

Lindy appealed to Scott. 'I'm afraid it'll make me short of this white paper. I'm willing to pay for it if I can get some more. You see, it's for his printing.'

Scott smiled reassuringly. 'Don't worry about it. We'll buy more and you certainly won't be expected to pay for it. I'm taking Cheryl to Napier on Friday. Apparently she needs extra clothes for her second week here. If you wish you may come and do some shopping for extra paper.'

'Can I come too?' Danny asked eagerly.

'Only if you're a very very good boy.'

An exclamation of dismay escaped Cheryl. 'Oh, Scott, how could you ruin our day so easily? You promised we'd have it together.'

He looked at her with mild interest. 'Did I indeed? If memory serves me correctly I think I happened to mention that I had to visit my accountant, and you then said you needed to collect extra clothes from home.'

Cheryl's lips pouted again. 'Oh, well, you know what I mean. I thought it'd be so nice to have time together beside the sea.'

'The sea,' Danny shouted in high glee. 'I want to go to the sea. Can I paddle in the water?'

'Definitely not, it's too cold,' Scott informed him.

'Ellie can come too?' Danny persisted.

'If she would like to,' Scott agreed.

But when Ellie received the invitation she shook her head and refused it politely. 'I was in Napier only last week,' she told Lindy. 'You see, I can go in with the mailman any time I wish to do so. I usually spend a night with my sister and return with the mailman next day. It's nice to be able to leave this place without having to rely on Scott or Steve. It takes away that feeling of isolation.'

Ellie's words gave Lindy something to think about, making her realise that if her situation at Whitecliffs became really unbearable she could make her escape with the assistance of the mailman. The knowledge gave her a sense of comfort which enabled her to face the following days with greater ease.

They passed quickly with Danny's lessons progressing

surprisingly well under the careful following of instructions in the Correspondence School books; nevertheless, when Friday came both teacher and pupil were grateful to be having a break from the confines of the tower room.

The day dawned with cloudless skies and frost on the grass. The snow-capped ranges glistened in the morning sun, and at nine o'clock the air was still stinging with icy freshness when Scott drove the Citroën to the front door.

Cheryl, wearing a smart outfit and wafting perfume, ran down the front steps to claim the passenger seat beside him. She then sent Lindy a superior smile which seemed to say the front seat was hers by divine right.

Lindy and Danny climbed into the back seat, and as they did so Ellie came down the steps to see them off. Her brown eyes took in the seating arrangements, then she spoke seriously to Scott.

'Are you wise to have Danny in the back seat? You know how he gets when the car swings round all those bends. It will be a pity if he throws up all over Cheryl's nice suit.'

Cheryl twisted in her seat to send a horrified glare towards Danny. 'Do you mean he gets *carsick*?'

'I'm afraid so,' Scott admitted nonchalantly. 'I was just about to suggest you changed places with him when Ellie beat me to it. I'd be glad if you'd swap seats.'

Cheryl was not amused. She left the front seat in sulky silence while Danny took her place with an air of importance.

And as the car moved from the steps Lindy caught the merest wink from Ellie. It made her want to giggle, but she managed to control her mirth by watching the passing landscape. As Ellie had reminded Scott, the country road was full of bends and it was a relief to reach Napier almost an hour later.

Scott drove Cheryl to her home which was a modest

house in one of the suburbs, and as she got out of the car she spoke anxiously to him. 'You will come back for me?'

'Of course. We'll be here at five o'clock,' he promised. 'Have a pleasant day with your mother.'

Cheryl's answering look told him plainly enough that she hadn't expected to be spending the day with her mother. She flashed a resentful glance towards Lindy, then vanished through a gateway.

Lindy felt embarrassed by her attitude. 'I'm sorry if my presence has ruined your day with Cheryl,' she felt compelled to say.

Scott made no reply, his silence making her feel even more embarrassed. Oh blast, she thought miserably, trying to rid herself of her intense mortification.

Danny then peered up into Scott's face. 'Uncle Scott, why is Cheryl at our place? Will she live with us for ever and ever?'

Lindy waited anxiously for his reply which seemed to be a long time in coming, but at last he leaned towards the boy and said quietly, 'At present she's my armour. Someday you'll understand what that means.'

Lindy was puzzled. Sitting in the back seat she'd had a little difficulty in catching the pronunciation of the word he had used. Had he meant armour—for protection? It seemed unlikely. Or had he meant *amour*, meaning a love affair?

Of course, that would be it, she decided sadly as a cold hand seemed to clutch at her heart.

CHAPTER SEVEN

WHEN they reached the city Scott guided Lindy to a shop that sold school equipment. Purchases were made, and with the parcels in the car they drove to the seafront where a long line of tall Norfolk pines stretched along the Parade.

He cruised slowly along its length to enable Lindy to view the well-kept gardens and the variety of entertainments provided for adults and children. Beyond them lay the slanting grey shingle shore which was being pounded by waves that rolled before sweeping down into a dangerous backwash.

Scott found a parking place within easy walking distance of the swings, and as they got out of the car he said, 'You'll be all right while I visit my accountant? I'll be with him for an hour or more, and then I'll take you to lunch.'

She nodded, smiling at him, but as she watched his tall figure stride away she was immediately swamped by loneliness She told herself she was being ridiculous, that she had Danny with her, but it was a bereft kind of loneliness that Danny's presence did nothing to compensate.

He tugged at her coat, at the same time hopping with impatience. 'Can we go to the swings?'

'Yes, of course, darling.' She turned to go and it was then she noticed a tall fair man watching them from across the road.

He stood on the edge of the pavement, his legs apart, his hands stuffed deeply in his pockets as he gazed at them intently. But it wasn't the first time a man had stared at Lindy, therefore she found no difficulty in ignoring him as she followed Danny who had raced ahead towards the swings.

Making her way to a seat she watched Danny's activities as he tried first one swing and then another, but suddenly a spasm of apprehension gripped her as she noticed that the man from across the road had also made his way towards the children's swing area. Had he deliberately followed them?

'Hi, kid,' he called in a friendly manner to Danny.

'Hi,' Danny shouted back. 'Will you give me a push so I can go high as the sky?'

The man obliged for a short time and as he did so Lindy observed him more closely.

He was about Scott's age, she decided. His clothes were well-cut and he seemed to be a respectable type. She also realised his interest appeared to lie more in Danny than in herself, although she was not surprised when he left the swings to sit beside her on the seat.

She was not in the habit of speaking to male strangers, therefore she continued to ignore him. However, she also realised there were plenty of empty seats near the swings, and this fact made her wonder why he hadn't taken one of them. Why had he come to sit beside her?

Instinct warned her there was a purpose behind his action, and, suddenly nervous, she was about to move to another seat when the man spoke to her.

'That boy is young Danny Reid, I think?'

Surprised, she turned to look at him. 'Yes. Do you know him?'

A wry grin twisted his mouth. 'I should, but I don't.'

'Then how do you know he is Danny?'

'Because I saw you both get out of Wardell's car. Are you his wife?' He glanced at her ringless hand. 'No, I see you're not.'

'So what's all this about? What's your interest in Danny?'

'I was just curious to have a look at him,' he said evasively.

Looking at the man's blue eyes and cast of features a germ of suspicion began to grow in her mind. This was no ordinary pick-up, she realised. 'Would you like to talk to him?' she offered.

'No, no, I don't want to get too close to him. He looks well and healthy,' he added with a note of satisfaction.

'He fretted after the death of his mother, but tender loving care is helping him to become well and normal again.' She sent him a side glance. 'You knew his mother had died, I presume?'

'Yes, I heard, but only recently, because I've been in Australia for the last few years.' He paused before saying thoughtfully, 'It must be getting near time for the boy's schooling.'

Lindy told him about the Correspondence School lessons and her own part in them. She then added, 'Are you sure you don't wish to talk to him?'

'No, I'm quite happy just to be watching him.'

The last remark confirmed her suspicions. 'Are you afraid to look him in the eye, Mr Reid? You are his father, aren't you?' It was really a shot in the dark but it worked.

The man turned startled eyes to stare at her. 'How did you guess?' he demanded gruffly.

'It wasn't difficult. There's a strong likeness between you and the mere fact of your interest in the boy was sufficient to tell me the truth. Why did you desert Adrianne?' she demanded coldly.

'I didn't desert her,' he gritted savagely. 'In actual fact she deserted me. She wouldn't come to Australia with me.'

'You—you really did ask her to go with you?'

'*Ask?* I damn well *pleaded* with her. I'm unaware of how much you know, but if you know only a part of it you might as well know the lot. These are the facts. Soon after we were married I had the opportunity to go into a mining venture in the outback of New South Wales, opals and that sort of thing, but would Adrianne come with me? Not for one moment would she consider it.'

'I wonder why?' Lindy pondered.

'Because she wouldn't go so far away from Wardell, of course,' he told her bitterly. 'We were living in a house I'd bought in Napier, and she could still visit Whitecliffs when it suited her.'

Lindy felt bewildered. 'But surely you were more important to her than Scott?'

'Can't you understand? She married me only because she thought she couldn't have him. She believed he was in love with her redheaded girlfriend who told her that she and Wardell were secretly engaged and that they'd been to bed on numerous occasions.'

Lindy flushed at the man's frankness. 'I don't—no, *I don't believe it*,' she said hotly. Nevertheless her mind jumped to the easy access from Scott's room to the one she now occupied, which had previously been used by Cheryl. And she also recalled Cheryl's annoyance on discovering she was unable to occupy it during her present visit.

Daniel Reid said, 'I don't believe it either. It's not in Wardell's character to be secretive about anything. He's an out-in-the-open type. But Adrianne was gullible, and that bitch Cheryl had her convinced, so she married me.'

Lindy felt shaken by the man's story which, she realised, echoed with a loud ring of truth. However, there was more she wished to learn. 'What are your plans, Mr Reid? Have you now returned to New Zealand permanently?'

'No, my interests in Aussie are too good to leave. This is just a flying visit to attend to a few business affairs. The house I own is to be sold and the money invested for the boy. I've also set up a trust for Danny.'

'You don't intend to take him back with you?'

'Certainly not. He's better off at Whitecliffs than with me in the Aussie outback. My solicitor will get in touch with Wardell. He'll be informed that Danny is no longer a pauper who relies on his charity. The trust will take care of all boarding-school fees which will be necessary later, to say nothing of the odd fancy he may have for an expensive horse or motor-bike.'

She could only look at him in silence.

He went on, 'I'm glad I've been able to see him. Actually, it was a stroke of luck. The Citroën caught my eye as I was coming out of my solicitor's office. Wardell always drove a Citroën so of course I took a second look at it, and then I could hardly believe my eyes when I saw him get out of it. Naturally I guessed the boy's identity, so I followed you.'

'You're sure you won't speak to him?' Lindy persisted.

He shook his head. 'I'd want to cuddle him and he'd object to it from a stranger. I'd shed tears and look an idiot. I might even blurt out that I'm his father and then have to leave him. You see, it's really the *leaving* him that'd be the trouble. No, it's better this way.' He stood up. 'It's time I got moving. I've a lot to do. It's been great to have had a look at him.'

As he began to move away Lindy said, 'Wait, there's just one more thing. Sooner or later he'll begin asking questions about his father. What shall we tell him?'

'Tell him the truth, and when he's old enough he can cross the Tasman to take a look at the Australian outback.' He gave her a penetrating look. 'I believe you're really fond of the boy.'

'I think I can say I love little Danny,' she said simply.

'You'll do your best for him?' he pleaded gruffly.

'Of course, you can rely on it,' she said sincerely.

'Good. In that case I'd like you to accept this as a reminder of that promise.' His fingers went to an inner pocket and drew forth a small tissue-wrapped object which he placed in her hand. 'Examine it after I've gone. You'll find it's quite a good one.' The next moment he'd left the area to vanish along the path leading back towards the town.

Lindy sat staring in front of her. The encounter had been like a dream, but as she watched Danny swinging backwards and forwards she knew it had been real. The small object in her hand was proof enough, and removing its wrapping carefully she gave a small gasp as the vivid reds, blues and greens of a large opal flashed in the sun. 'I can't believe it,' she murmured, fingering its smoothness, then hastily rewrapped the gem and put it safely in her handbag.

A short time later Danny became tired of the swings, so Lindy led him to where he could watch children and adults speeding round a rink on roller-skates. But while he was fascinated by their activities she herself hardly saw them, her mind being entirely engrossed by the recent encounter and the revelations made by Daniel Reid. Were they true? Instinct told her they were.

So Adrianne *had* been in love with Scott, she realised. Nor was this really surprising. But Scott had felt only friendship towards her, as he'd already stated. And then Cheryl's whispered information had driven Adrianne into the arms of another man. Later, when Scott failed to commit himself to Cheryl, Adrianne had realised her mistake. She'd become frustrated, and when Daniel had tried to remove her from the scene, to the distant Australian outback, she'd refused to go.

Now the situation was repeating itself, and it was almost as if she herself had taken Adrianne's place by falling in love with Scott. She was attending to Danny's lessons in the same manner in which Adrianne would have guided him, and once again Cheryl had come into the arena. Would Scott make a definite commitment to the beautiful redhead this time? The thought sent Lindy's spirits plunging downward.

Pondering deeply, she was unaware of his approach until he spoke.

'Hullo there, you look as if you're in a dream.'

His deep voice startled her, while the sight of him made her heart pound and the blood rush to her face.

He looked at her flushed cheeks, then said softly, 'Those thoughts must've been interesting. Care to share them?'

She shook her head, glanced at Danny and said, 'Not at present.'

Danny then relieved the situation by declaring himself to be hungry, so Scott took them to a restaurant at the end of the Parade. Surrounded by gardens, it was a circular building with windows overlooking the sea and a long stretch of stony beach, and it was as they sat enjoying a delicious fish meal that Danny looked up at Scott and said, 'Lindy talked to a man.'

Scott smiled at the boy. 'Did she indeed?' The grey eyes then held a question as they turned to Lindy. 'You met someone you know?'

'No. A man came to sit beside me on the seat.'

Scott frowned. 'He tried to pick you up?'

'Oh no, he just wanted to talk.'

'Really? About what, may I ask?'

'Oh, about a certain little person with big ears,' she replied vaguely. 'Now is not the moment—you understand?'

The dark brows drew together again. 'You mean——?' His glance flicked to Danny, who was watching a seagull through the window.

She nodded, hoping he would not pursue the subject.

'This is what caused you to be in such deep thought when I arrived? I wondered if you were in a trance.'

'I think I was, almost,' she confessed reluctantly.

Danny turned to Lindy with a question that had apparently been bothering him. 'Why do little people have big ears?' he asked.

'So they can listen when someone has a strange story to tell,' she prevaricated, avoiding Scott's eyes.

His regard became piercing. 'Does this—er—strange story happen to concern me in any way?' he drawled in a soft voice that dripped with suspicion.

'Yes, quite closely,' she admitted, knowing that sooner or later the facts of the trust would come to light.

'I notice you haven't yet told me the identity of this fellow.'

'Nor do I intend to at present. May we change the subject?'

'Okay, we'll leave it for the moment but you'll give me the whole queer story later. Is that understood?'

His voice held that note of command she was beginning to know so well. It caused her to look at him doubtfully, knowing it would be difficult to tell him everything Daniel Reid had said, especially about Adrianne and Cheryl.

He said, 'We'll go up into the tower after dinner.'

'That's if you can escape from Cheryl,' she remarked, forcing an innocent smile.

His voice became cool. 'Are you suggesting I'm unable to do that? You're making a mistake.'

'It's obvious you find difficulty in doing so, but it's also possible you have no *wish* to do so.' It was an effort to control her runaway tongue before it could betray the jealousy gnawing at her soul.

They left the restaurant and spent the rest of the afternoon moving between the various marine entertainments on the Parade. Danny shrieked with delight as dolphins leapt into the air or clapped their flippers, and he gazed wide-eyed at the aquarium's exotic fish swimming in glass-fronted tanks.

In the shell department Lindy admired the iridescent blues, greens, pinks and mauves that gleamed on a jewel-box covered by the New Zealand paua shell.

Scott immediately bought it for her. 'Does receiving a small gift always make your eyes shine?' he asked teasingly.

'It depends who gives——' She swallowed and fell silent, then glanced at her watch to discover the hours had flown. 'It's almost four o'clock,' she told him, making an effort to keep the acute disappointment from her voice.

After that it seemed to be only minutes before the Citroën was heading towards Cheryl's home, and even when still a distance from the house they could see her waiting at the gate with two large suitcases beside her.

The smile she sent Scott was radiant. 'I knew you'd be dead on time, that you wouldn't delay a moment in picking me up.'

Lindy watched his face and wondered about the grimness lining his mouth. She felt the car shudder slightly as he dumped the two heavy cases in the boot, and through the open window his voice came clearly, tinged, she thought, with a touch of sarcasm.

'I thought a change of clothes was all you wanted. You look as though you're moving in permanently.'

Cheryl gave a tinkling laugh. 'I will if you'd like me to. Just say the word.'

Lindy knew the gay teasing tone was meant to indicate she was only joking, but she also guessed that Cheryl meant every word. A cold ball of despair seemed to form in her stomach, causing her to sit in misery during the journey home.

Nor was there any comfort to be derived when Danny, that small imparter of news, turned to Cheryl and said, 'Uncle Scott gave Lindy a pretty box. It's all shining with lots and lots of colours.'

Cheryl sent Lindy a glance that was full of suspicion but managed to control her curiosity.

Scott silenced Danny with a sharp word, making Lindy wonder if he had no wish for the gift to be discussed in front of Cheryl, and as he stepped on the gas the car sped home.

In the privacy of her room Lindy took the paua shell box from its wrapping and hugged it to her before fingering its colourful smoothness. She knew she would always treasure it, and only her more valuable pieces of jewellery would be kept in it.

She went to dinner with a lighter heart, but as the meal progressed she began to feel apprehensive about the coming session in the tower. The stranger's identity would have to be admitted, and then Scott would demand to know everything the man had said.

It would be easy enough to tell him of the trust being set up for Danny, but there was no way in which she could tell him the rest. How could she let him know that Adrianne had loved him, but had turned to Daniel Reid because of the alliance between Cheryl and himself? Had they been spending hours in bed? No, she refused to believe it, because the thought was like a knife twisting in her heart. It made her go cold with misery.

However, before the meal was finished a different problem was placed before Scott, and for a short time Lindy imagined it would occupy his mind for the rest of the evening. It was brought to light when Steve made an abrupt statement.

'We're losing Eric Briggs.'

Scott frowned. 'Oh? Is he dissatisfied with his job here?'

'No, but he happens to have been offered a good one near his mother-in-law. His wife is keen for him to take it because she doesn't see much of her mother who is in poor health.'

'I'll be sorry to lose Briggs, he's a darned good man with sheep,' Scott said. 'It means finding someone else.'

'He says he'll stay until you're fixed with a new man, but in the meantime he'd like you to consider his friend, John Roberts, who has to find a new job.'

'Why should he have to do that?' Scott asked.

'The property he's on has been sold to a man with two adult sons who make John's presence superfluous. But wait, there's something else. The Robertses have a six-year-old who is driven to school each day by Mrs Roberts, and the same routine could be carried out here. Eric Briggs suggested that she could pick Danny up as well,' Steve added casually.

Cheryl made no effort to hide her eagerness. 'That's marvellous. It's the answer to Danny's schooling problem,' she exclaimed with thinly veiled satisfaction.

Scott sat back in his chair and regarded Lindy through half-closed lids. 'What does his present teacher think about the situation? That's if it comes to pass.'

'Cheryl's right, of course. It's the answer. And there's something else, Danny would have a playmate near home, and that would be lovely for him,' Lindy replied.

Steve's face took on a cheerful expression. 'I knew Lindy would see it that way. She knows it'll be the end of her job here, but she understands perfectly and wants only the best for the boy.'

As she listened to his words she knew an inward feeling of relief. Steve, it seemed, no longer cared whether or not she was at Whitecliffs, and this meant he was unlikely to pester her with any more amorous attentions. Turning to him she said, 'You're forgetting that my time here is limited.'

Scott cut in, '—and in any case it'll be at least a month before the new man can start, because notice must be given to his present employer. But first I'll talk to Eric Briggs about him. After all, I haven't even been given his formal notice yet. We're really way ahead of ourselves.'

Matters concerning the change of sheep manager

continued to be discussed until the end of the meal, and then, as they rose to lift the dishes from the table to the trolley, Scott glanced at Lindy and said, 'You and I will now carry the school parcels up to the tower.'

'I'll help you,' Cheryl offered brightly. 'There seemed to be so many.' She moved towards the hall where the pile of parcels had been left.

Scott put out a detaining hand. 'No thank you, Cheryl,' he said firmly. 'Lindy and I have private matters to discuss, so you and Steve can occupy yourselves by pushing the dishes out to Ellie. You might even help her by stacking them into the dishwasher.'

Cheryl stared at him aghast. *'In this dress?'*

'You could try putting on an apron,' he grinned.

They carried the parcels up to the tower and after dumping the heaviest of them on the table Scott turned to face her. 'Okay, let's have it.' His tone was abrupt and demanding, his mouth grim, and his grey eyes seemed to bore into her mind. 'Tell me about this fellow.'

'I think you've already guessed the man's identity,' she said.

'The mere fact that you wouldn't discuss him openly in front of Danny made me suspicious. Was it Reid, his father?'

'Yes. He happened to see us get out of the car. He recognised you and knew the boy must be Danny.'

'Well, where has he been all this time?'

'Gem-mining in the Australian outback. He gave me an opal. It's really a bribe to do my best for Danny.'

'An opal! You must've become mighty matey in a damned short time. I'm surprised you accepted it.' His voice had become icy.

His scathing tone stung. 'You don't understand that I had little option. He put it in my hand as he was about to leave, and before I could look at it he'd disappeared.

I'm sorry if it sounds lame, but that's what happened.' Then, glaring at him she added. 'Or do you think I should've left Danny while I went searching for him along the Parade?'

'Okay, so he gave you an opal,' he gritted. 'What else?'

'Nothing, of course. What else would he give me?'

'I didn't mean that and you know it. What else did he have to *say*?' he snapped impatiently.

'Oh, well, he wanted to know about Danny's schooling, so I told him about my part in it.'

'And so he gave you an opal,' he repeated, furiously this time.

She looked at him steadily. 'Would you mind telling me why you're so annoyed about it?'

He gripped her shoulders and gave her a slight shake. 'Because I can't stand the thought of that fellow giving you *anything*. It makes me mad.'

Her heart leapt. Surely he couldn't be jealous? 'Why should it make you mad?' she felt compelled to ask.

His hands dropped from her shoulders as he brushed her question aside. 'Never mind about that. Tell me more of what he said.'

Memory of the house sale and the trust that had been formed sprang into her mind and she was thankful to be able to expand a little on the reasons for Daniel Reid's visit to Napier. At last she said, 'Sooner or later you'll be given the details of the trust through his solicitor.' She fell silent after her last words.

'And that's all?' he demanded, watching her closely.

The rest of Daniel Reid's revelations sprang through her memory. *Had he been sleeping with Cheryl during those nights?* Her eyes were wide as she turned to face him. 'It's all I prefer to talk about,' she admitted at last. 'I'd prefer to forget the rest.' It had been an unwise statement to make, she realised, but the words had just slipped out and now she looked at him nervously.

'The rest? What the hell do you mean by the *rest*?'

'I've nothing further to say. Let's go downstairs.'

'Not yet,' he rasped. 'I intend to learn what it is you'd prefer to forget.'

'And I've no intention of telling you.' She moved towards the door and although he put out a hand to grab her arm she skipped away, dodged round him and fled down the stairs. She was in the lounge almost before he'd left the tower, and moments later she thought she heard the slam of his office door.

'Where's Scott?' Cheryl demanded.

Lindy shrugged. 'In his office, I think.'

'Does your red face mean you've had a row?'

Lindy's chin rose. 'Certainly not, please mind your own business.'

'Ha, ha, I can tell you've had a row. Put you in your place, did he? Good for him.'

'Shut up, Cheryl.' The reprimand came from Steve who was watching television. 'Come and sit here, Lindy.'

But Lindy felt she'd had enough. 'No, thank you, I think I'll go to bed and read.' Her legs felt shaky as she left the room.

But when she lay back against the pillows she was unable to become interested in the book. Instead she relived the minutes with Daniel Reid, trying to recall in detail everything he'd said about Scott, Adrianne and Cheryl. The thought of Scott and Cheryl in bed together gnawed at her very soul—*this* actual bed, she felt sure, so that when Scott entered her room through the adjoining bathroom a gasp escaped her. She sat up and gaped at him, the blankets clutched tightly beneath her chin.

'I didn't think you'd take advantage of those doors,' she protested, staring at him wide-eyed.

'Discretion is necessary when others are in the house,' he replied blandly as he sat on the side of the bed.

'Surely you realise our conversation in the tower was cut short by your hasty departure.'

'But I'd told you—all that was necessary.'

'I doubt it.'

'I don't know what else——'

'I think you do. Is it so strange that I should want to know the rest of Reid's conversation? He must've mentioned Adrianne.'

'Well, yes, he mentioned her,' she admitted warily.

'For Pete's sake, why do I have to drag it out of you?'

She looked at him in silence, wondering about Cheryl.

'I suppose it's too much to expect him to have told you what went wrong between them, why he left her at such an early stage in their marriage. He must've known she was pregnant.'

'I'm afraid he puts the blame on Adrianne. Apparently she refused to go to Australia with him.'

'Rubbish. I don't believe it.'

Her shoulders lifted in a small shrug. 'I can only tell you what he said, and he seemed very sincere about it.'

'But *why*? If he had a good opportunity it doesn't make sense.'

Lindy paused, searching for words until at last she said carefully, 'The people she loved were in this country. She could not bear the thought of—of leaving them for such a distant place.'

'I don't recall her being over-fond of her aunt.'

'No?'

'In fact she spent most of her time here, at Whitecliffs.'

'No doubt. I wonder why?' Lindy murmured drily.

He looked at her sharply. 'Are you suggesting she was here only because of someone in particular?'

She sent him a level glance. 'Well, wasn't she?'

'I don't believe there was anything between Adrianne and Steve.'

'*That* I can believe. And I dare say you can discount Bert.'

'Then are you suggesting that I had anything to do with her refusal to go with Reid?' His words had been dangerously quiet before erupting into anger. 'Didn't I tell you we were just good friends?'

'Did it never occur to you that the good-friend attitude might have been on your part only?'

'Is that what Reid said?'

Again she remained silent.

Exasperated, he said, 'If you don't come clean and tell me the whole story I'll—I'll drag you out of that bed.' His hands on the blankets indicated that the threat was real.

Fear made her say hurriedly, 'All right, I'll tell you. Mr Reid was sure Adrianne was in love with you.'

'Absolute rot. She married *him*, didn't she?'

'Only because she was given to understand that you were in love with—with somebody else. In fact, according to him, she was given to understand you were about to announce your engagement.' She drew a deep breath as the fact of having told him seemed to lift a weight from her mind.

His eyes glittered from behind slits. 'Who the hell would tell her such damned nonsense?' he gritted.

'I'm afraid you'll have to decide that question for yourself.' She'd said quite enough, she felt.

He gripped her by the shoulders and shook her roughly. 'Does this mean you're refusing to tell me?'

'You're hurting me,' she protested, struggling to keep the blankets beneath her chin.

'Tell me or I'll——' He ripped the bedding down to her waist, then gazed at the mounds of breasts rising beneath the soft gathers of pink brushed nylon nightdress.

She crossed her arms in an effort to conceal herself. 'I'm sorry, I can't tell you anything further,' she whispered, her eyes filling with tears. And while her expression became one of pathos it gave no indication of the thoughts squirming about in her mind.

Thinking of Cheryl's part in the affair Lindy knew she held a weapon that could be used against her, except that it was not in her nature to do so. It was also possible that Scott loved Cheryl, but was still unsure of the depth of his feelings, and the knowledge of her part in causing Adrianne to turn to Daniel Reid would only infuriate him.

'Come on, out with it,' he snapped.

Her eyes glistened like twin pools as the tears trickled down her cheeks, but they had little effect on him.

'Don't try that sob stuff on me, because it won't work,' he snarled. 'I want to know who fed lies to Adrianne. Are you going to tell me?'

'I'd rather not,' she whispered. 'You'd be terribly hurt. Please believe me, it's best forgotten.'

'Very well,' he snapped with what appeared to be a sudden capitulation. 'It's obvious you're protecting somebody, and that person can only be Ellie.'

She was horrified. '*Ellie*? Of course it isn't Ellie. How could you possibly think such a thing of her?' Shocked tones echoed her indignation.

'Then that leaves Cheryl, doesn't it?' he accused softly.

She fell silent, suddenly aware of the trap he'd set. 'Please, Scott, I'm telling you *it's best forgotten*,' she repeated. 'You can't do anything about it. It's finished, over and done with, water under the bridge.'

'What did she tell Adrianne?' he demanded in cold flat tones.

She shook her head and remained silent.

'Okay, I'd have to be mighty dumb if I couldn't make a damned shrewd guess at that one. No doubt she told Adrianne I wore a track between our two rooms?'

'Mr Reid understands it was—something like that. Is it true?' She was unable to resist the question.

'What do you think, Lindy Farrell?'

'Surely you're not suggesting that my opinion would interest you?'

'I'm asking for it, aren't I?'

His voice had become bitter enough for her to recognise the tone of a man being unjustly accused. It caused her spirits to rise slightly, but still she remained non-committal.

'I had no right to ask if it were true,' she admitted. 'Your—affair—with Cheryl is not my business.' At least, not the affair of five years ago, she added silently to herself. But the affair of today was an entirely different matter.

CHAPTER EIGHT

WATCHING him Lindy waited for more to be said about the affair with Cheryl. She hoped he'd make explanations or, better still, deny the whole thing, but in this she was to be disappointed. Instead, he left the bedside and began to pace about the room.

When he did eventually speak it concerned a different matter. 'Where's the opal? I'd like to look at it.'

'It's in my handbag on the dressing-table. You'll find it wrapped in tissue paper.'

He passed the leather shoulder-bag to her. 'You find it,' he commanded, then sat on the bed again.

Her fingers shook slightly as she unwrapped the opal, and as it lay in her hand they both gazed at it in silence.

Scott was surprised by its size and depth of colour. 'It's a beauty,' he said at last turning it over. 'It's far too big for a ring but it could be set to make a lovely brooch or pendant. What will you do with it?'

'I thought I'd give it to Ellie. She's the one who has really looked after Danny. I think she's earned it.'

'You're right, but I presume Reid gave it to you in anticipation of what you'd be doing for him in the future.'

She smiled whimsically. 'He didn't know I'm here only on a month's trial, and that I'll be leaving in three weeks' time. And when Danny goes to school Ellie will still be taking care of him. I'm sure Mr Reid would agree if he knew the situation.'

'But he gave it to *you*. Obviously you appealed to him.'

'And I shall give it to Ellie,' she repeated with quiet determination. 'Of course, I'll have to tell her the story of our meeting.' She wrapped the opal in its tissue paper and replaced it in her handbag.

'Bless you, Lindy.' His voice was strangely husky as his arms went about her. 'You're quite right, Ellie more than deserves it. I'll have it set for her as a mark of my own appreciation.'

She leaned against him, her head resting against his breadth of shoulder. 'That would be very kind,' she murmured, revelling in the closeness of his embrace. Then, as he tipped her chin upwards, she breathed a long sigh of contentment as his mouth came down upon her own, demanding a response she was only too willing to give.

At first it was a gentle kiss that played with her lips coaxingly, making her feel drugged as it sent her heart thudding to a faster beat while her brain whirled dizzily.

'You're more than ready for love, Lindy,' his deep voice murmured in her ear.

Her arms went about him and his lips found hers again, deepening to a kiss of more passionate demands which sent unaccustomed spasms of desire shooting through every fibre of her body. Her fingers fondled the dark hair at the nape of his neck while his mouth moved to trace a line to her throat, then caressed its way downward to the swell of her breast now visible at the deep neckline of her nightdress.

For several minutes her mind floated aloft, soaring to giddy heights while she told herself that Scott was about to whisper words that would betray his depth of feeling for her. But when the words came they grated on her ears and sent her crashing to earth.

'Thank you for thinking of Ellie,' he said quietly. 'You could easily keep the opal for yourself. You realise it's quite valuable, I suppose?'

She remained perfectly still, silently cursing herself for being so vulnerable. So these kisses were mere gratitude for her gesture towards Ellie. 'Yes, being valuable makes the gift worthwhile,' she managed to say at last.

'I'm sure Ellie will appreciate it. I doubt that she has any jewellery that's as valuable as the brooch will be.'

You stupid fool, she chided herself mentally, drawing away from him and struggling to drag the blankets beneath her chin once more. You might've known his caresses had nothing to do with any depth of feeling he has for *you, you idiot*. Oh no, that'll be kept for *Cheryl*. She turned away, unable to look at him as a surge of jealousy made her shiver.

He looked at her intently. 'What's the matter? I felt you tremble. Are you cold?'

She nodded. 'Yes, a little. And I'm very tried.'

'Okay, I'll take the hint and let you go to sleep.'

She yearned to reach out and clasp him again, to beg him to stay because she didn't want to go to sleep. She wanted to say she longed to lie in his arms, but fearing that perhaps Cheryl was uppermost in his mind, how could she admit to these desires? There was only one thing she could do and she did it. She remained silent as she watched him return to his room through the bathroom doors.

After that sleep eluded her until, frustrated, she switched on the light above the bed and snatched up her book. But although she tried to read, the pages became blurred as the words failed to register, and then concentration had barely begun to manifest itself when a movement of the door leading into the passage caught her eye. Suddenly alert, she watched it open quietly and slowly until Cheryl, wearing a long pale-gold dressing-gown, stepped into the room.

Lindy watched her in silence as she waited for her to speak, but when Cheryl merely stood and stared about the room she felt compelled to ask, 'Are you looking for someone?'

'Of course I am. Actually, I'm looking for Scott. He usually says good night to me,' she said smugly.

'You thought he might be in here?'

'I thought I heard voices a short time ago.'

'So that's why you crept in without knocking?'

'Was he in here?' Cheryl demanded suspiciously.

'Yes. You probably heard us talking,' Lindy informed her calmly. 'We had quite a discussion.'

Cheryl's eyes widened. 'He was in here *while you were in bed*?'

'That's right,' Lindy smiled.

'Where is he now?' Cheryl demanded, her eyes again staring about the room.

Lindy giggled. 'You could try looking in the wardrobe or under the bed. Otherwise you might find him in his own bed.'

Cheryl didn't pursue the subject. Instead her attention became riveted on the paua shell box resting on the dressing-table. Lifting it up for closer inspection she said, 'This is the pretty box Danny referred to in the car?'

'Yes, I'm delighted with it.'

Cheryl replaced it with a slight bang, then moved nearer the bed. Glaring at Lindy she hissed angrily. 'You've got a nerve accepting a gift from Scott. Aren't you aware that we're engaged?'

'Really? I haven't noticed you wearing a ring.'

'You'll see it quite soon now.' Cheryl's tone was defiant.

Lindy's heart sank although she did her best to keep a brave front. 'I'll believe it when I see it, but not before.'

'I'm telling you, we're almost engaged to be married.'

'I think you told the same story to Adrianne, with a few additions. It was what turned her towards Daniel Reid. Remember?'

Cheryl's face became drained of its colour. 'Who told you that rubbish? I demand to know who told you or I'll—I'll——' Her voice shook as it rose to a higher pitch.

Lindy made an effort to remain calm. 'Yes? You'll what?'

'Or I'll slap your face,' Cheryl shouted, and adding action to the threat she sent a stinging blow across Lindy's cheek.

A cry of pain escaped Lindy as her hand flew to her face. She crouched back in the bed, fearing more blows, but as Cheryl's hand swung to deliver another slap Scott strode through the bathroom doorway.

'What the hell's going on?' he rasped angrily. His eyes were like cold grey pebbles as they rested upon Lindy's reddened cheek. 'Did she attack you?'

But Lindy had nothing to say. Her expression was woeful and full of guilt because she knew her remarks had provoked Cheryl to fury.

He turned to Cheryl. 'What the devil gets into you, you redheaded spitfire? I can see you've struck Lindy. What's this all about? I want to know the truth.'

Cheryl began to whimper. 'Scott darling, she was saying *beastly* things about me, accusing me of—of *dreadful* things, so I gave her what she deserves,' she finished defiantly.

'What are you doing in here?' His voice was cold.

'I came in here looking for you, even if I couldn't bear to find you here. It was to say good night. Scott darling, you didn't say good night to me.' Her arms went about his neck and she lifted her face as she clung to him.

He did not kiss her. Instead, he released himself from her embrace and said in clipped tones, 'Okay, I'll say it now. *Good night.* Go to bed. And if you attack Lindy again you'll be packing your bags right smartly.'

'She's the one who should be packing her bags,' Cheryl snapped furiously. 'She was hinting at things about—*about us.*'

'I told you to go to bed,' he almost snarled.

Cheryl sent an angry glare towards Lindy, then flounced from the room.

There was a moment of silence before Scott turned to Lindy, again examining her flushed cheek. 'You're all right?'

She nodded wordlessly.

He sat on the bed beside her. 'Do you want to talk about it?'

She shook her head. 'I'd rather not.'

He did not press the point. Instead he picked up the book on the bedside table. 'Perhaps you'd be wise to read for a while. It helps one to sleep.'

The robe he wore had fallen open to reveal the short dark hairs on his chest. She longed to touch them, to feel their crispness, but to do so would make it obvious she wanted his arms about her again, which of course was true.

What would happen if she put her own arms about him? Would he respond? Or would he treat her as abruptly as he'd treated Cheryl? His brusque manner towards Cheryl had really surprised her, but even as she pondered this fact he stood up and spoke curtly.

'I'll leave you to settle down. Good night.'

She watched him disappear through the bathroom door and as he closed it behind him she found herself wishing he'd at least kissed her once more. But after all why should he? He had no real depth of feeling for her. She knew that now. And with this bitter knowledge her tears fell into the pillow.

During the next fortnight June slid into July. The weather became colder with heavy snow whitening the ranges down to three thousand feet above sea level, while the muddy swollen river raced along the foot of the cliffs as though anxious to be away from the place.

At the end of each day the men came in to shed their damp, chilly clothes before standing beneath the comfort of hot showers. After dinner each night they relaxed before a roaring fire in the lounge, and it was during these periods that Lindy learnt there was little or no growth in the grass, and that the evening sky had warned them about the next day's weather.

Food for the animals seemed to be the dominant topic of conversation, and listening to it she also learnt it was necessary to feed hay to the deer and to dribble long lines of grain across the fields. The sheep were being moved into enclosures of swedes, turnips or green crops grown especially for winter feed.

But although she didn't see much of the outside world the days failed to drag because she was busily occupied with Danny's lessons.

One wet afternoon the little boy stood at the window and gazed down at the mist-covered riverflats. 'When can I fly my kite again, Lindy?' he pleaded.

'On the first suitable day,' she promised.

'When is it going to stop raining?' he asked wistfully as the heavy drops pattered on the tower roof.

'When the clouds roll away and the sun begins to shine. Now come back to the table and we'll talk about green bottles.' Then, as he returned to his seat beside her she began to quote, 'There were ten green bottles hanging on the wall, ten green bottles hanging on the wall, if one green bottle should accidently fall there'd be nine green bottles hanging on the wall. Nine green bottles——'

The ditty continued until the last green bottle had fallen, and the exercise was then applied to sheep when pupil and teacher knelt on the floor beside the plastic farm with its animals and sheds.

Lindy said, 'Here we have ten sheep in the field, but this one has found a hole in the fence. It has got out, so how many sheep are left in the field?'

'*Nine,*' he shouted after careful consideration.

'Good boy,' she praised. 'Ten, take away one leaves nine.'

However, Danny was not the only person to find the

wintry weather irksome. Cheryl was bored and made no effort to conceal her irritation at the fact that Scott was refusing to take her riding with him. She spent hours in his office browsing through books until this failed to interest her, and as a last resort she turned to Lindy with a show of friendship.

It began slowly with more conversation than usual being directed towards Lindy, and then came the day when Cheryl mounted the stairs and entered the schoolroom.

'I've come to relieve you,' she said with a smile. 'I think you need a rest from all this work with Danny.'

Lindy was startled by the suggestion. 'I don't need a rest, thank you, nor do I expect to be relieved.' She bent over the letters Danny had been printing.

'I'm only trying to help,' Cheryl insisted. 'Surely you'd like a break to do something else like—like helping Ellie.'

'No, thank you, my work is here.' Lack of trust where Cheryl was concerned kept her voice cool.

Cheryl's white teeth bit into her lower lip. 'Look here, I can understand your stand-offish attitude, but I'm only trying to bridge the gap between us. I'm sorry I've been bitchy to you, and I'm sorry I slapped you that night. I can see now that I was mistaken. Can't we be friends?'

Lindy remained silent for several minutes. She knew Cheryl was watching her anxiously, and suddenly she decided she was being churlish. If Cheryl could offer a hand of friendship, surely she could extend her own to grasp it.

The decision brought a smile to her face. 'Very well, let's be friends,' she agreed. 'I must admit I'd be glad to see the end of the antagonism you've held towards me.'

'I'll make up for it,' Cheryl promised. 'Really, I will. As soon as this ghastly rain stops I'll give you a riding lesson on old Meg. She's really too quiet for me. I've reached the stage of wanting a much more lively horse, but Meg is excellent for learning to ride.'

Lindy looked at her wonderingly. 'You'll really give me a riding lesson? I'd be so grateful.'

'I'll give you several. We'll start you off bareback to give you balance. Just wait for the first fine day.'

But when the rain ceased and the sun shone on the glistening wet countryside Cheryl's promise appeared to have been forgotten. Dressed in her jodhpurs and warm jacket she rode away beside Scott, and again Lindy stood watching them through the kitchen window.

Ellie, who stood beside her, sighed with exasperation. 'I can't understand why he keeps that girl here. Really, he's got me completely puzzled.'

'It seems simple enough to me.' The words came from Bert who had entered the kitchen with a basket of firewood.

Ellie turned to face him. 'Is that so, Bert Price? Well, I've known you to be right on more than one occasion, so what's your reasoning this time?'

'He's protecting himself, that's all.'

'*Protecting* himself? What utter rubbish.'

Bert frowned. 'Woman, if you can't take my opinion, don't ask for it. I'm telling you, he's doing his best to remain *free*. He doesn't want to become involved.'

'Then he's going about it in a mighty funny way,' Ellie snapped.

'Is he? Work it out for yourself. He's using Cheryl as a sort of shield from somebody else.' His eyes slid momentarily towards Lindy before he took the wood to the lounge fire.

'Do you know what he means?' Lindy asked timidly.

'I'm not sure,' Ellie said thoughtfully. 'I can only imagine he means that Scott is using Cheryl's company to guard against seeing too much of *you*. Apparently he doesn't wish to become involved with *anyone*. I can only hope that Cheryl doesn't trap him into becoming committed to her.'

Lindy's face became dismal as she recalled Cheryl's words in the bedroom. 'We're almost engaged,' she had declared. *Was it true this time?*

The next few days continued to be fine but without any further suggestion of riding lessons. Nor did Lindy feel inclined to remind Cheryl of her promise, and a sense of depression gripped her as, day after day, she watched helplessly while Scott took the beautiful redhead out on the farm with him.

But after all, what did it matter? Her month's trial was drawing to a close and she'd be returning to Wellington. In the meantime Cheryl continued to show a friendly attitude towards her, and this became so obvious it drew comment from Scott.

'You girls appear to be getting along really well,' he remarked at breakfast on what would be Lindy's last Monday morning. 'Have you at last discovered each other's virtues?' The grey eyes moved from one to the other.

Lindy looked at her plate and said nothing, mainly because she was not too sure about Cheryl's virtues; nor was she confident there was any real depth in Cheryl's display of friendship.

But Cheryl was quick to assure Scott on this point. 'Oh yes, we've become the *best* of friends. Lindy is such a *sweet* person, she's really doing her best for Danny. I offered to give her a rest by relieving her for a day, but would she be prised away from her beloved pupil? Oh no, not likely. I really believe she's just a teeny-weeny bit jealous of the fact that I'll be taking over Danny when her month is up.' Cheryl's quiet laugh indicated her confidence.

Scott looked at her gravely. 'That was very kind of you, Cheryl. You actually offered to relieve Lindy for a day?'

'Yes, yes I did. Isn't that so, Lindy?' She turned

eagerly, pleading for confirmation.

Lindy nodded as she watched Scott's handsome face. She must savour these precious moments of sitting with him at the breakfast table, she realised. Soon they'd be only a memory. And then his next words swept the thoughts from her mind. In fact they amazed her to the extent of leaving her speechless.

Regarding Cheryl intently he said, 'In that case you'll be given the opportunity to relieve her today.'

Cheryl looked at him sharply. 'Oh? What do you mean? What's so important about relieving her today?'

'I'll be taking her with me while I interview Roberts, the man Eric Briggs has suggested I employ. It's the first chance I've had to do so. He lives a few miles out of Waipawa.'

Cheryl's jaw dropped slightly as her eyes narrowed. 'Why take Lindy?' she demanded with a faint show of temper. 'I'm the one who should be going with you.' Her voice had risen to a higher note.

'Why?' Scott put the question bluntly.

'Because—because——' Cheryl flushed and fell silent. 'Why should you take Lindy?' she countered defiantly.

'Because I'll be glad of her opinion. I want her to meet Mrs Roberts, who'll be driving Danny to school.' He looked at her in a thoughtful manner, then added pointedly, 'And who'll make it unnecessary to have a teacher in the house.'

'Oh.' Cheryl was taken aback. 'Well, what's so important about Lindy's opinion? What's wrong with mine?'

He smiled at her kindly, then patted her hand. 'I do not have to explain my reasons to anyone. You offered to relieve Lindy for a day—so here's your big chance to do so.'

Cheryl pouted, then groped in her mind for further objections. 'You know Steve will be furious with you.' She looked about her. 'Where is he?'

Ellie supplied the answer. She had been hovering in the background and now came forward. 'Steve went out quite early and Bert went with him.' She turned to Scott. 'Did you say you're going near Waipawa? I've a huge list of groceries to be bought. If you're taking Lindy I'm sure she wouldn't mind finding things for you in the supermarket.'

Lindy took the long list from her, checking to make sure she could decipher Ellie's handwriting. The action helped to cover the fact that she was completely dazed. Scott was taking her out and she could hardly believe it. He was actually taking *her* instead of Cheryl.

She hastened to her room and changed from her slacks to more feminine attire of jersey and skirt, attended to her make-up, then snatched up her jacket and shoulder-bag. By the time she had hurried along the passage the Citroën was waiting at the front door and as she took her seat beside Scott she was almost quivering with excitement.

He turned to regard her intently. 'Is something wrong? You appear to be quite jittery.'

She managed to smile at him. 'Nothing's wrong. It's only the shock of being asked to come with you.' It was an effort to keep her voice steady.

'Are you saying you don't wish to come?'

'Oh no,' she hastened to assure him. 'It's just that you appear to be so rapt in Cheryl's company. I wouldn't like to intrude.'

He frowned. '*Rapt? Intrude?* Hell's bells.'

'Yes, I think rapt would be the better word.'

'Hmm.' He paused then asked, 'You don't object to Cheryl taking over Danny for the day?'

She laughed. 'Do you mean, am I jealous, as she suggested? Certainly not. He'll have to become used to different teachers. This is only the beginning.'

'Okay, let's get going.' The motor sang quietly as the

sleek French car glided down to the bridge, then sped up the hill to the boundary cattle-grid.

She remained silent while he negotiated the twists and turns of the narrow metalled back-country road, but when they reached the more even contour of the tarseal she felt compelled to ask a question.

'Scott, would you mind satisfying my curiosity?'

'Sure. What's bothering you?'

'Why am I here with you, instead of Cheryl?'

'Would you believe it was because I wanted you to be with me?'

His words caused her heart to give a crazy leap, but it was immediately stilled as the smile about his lips suggested he was merely having his little joke. And then she recalled his former words. 'You said something about wanting an opinion,' she reminded him.

'Yes. I want yours. While I'm interviewing Roberts I want you to talk to his wife. I want to know if you consider her to be a woman who'd get on well with Ellie. People in the back country rely on each other so much.'

'I see.'

'I want you to observe the state of the house they're living in.'

She was aghast. 'Are you saying you want me to *spy* on her?'

'You can put it that way if you wish, but just remember she'll be living in one of our houses.'

'*Our* houses? Don't you mean one of *your* houses?'

If he noticed the emphasis behind the question he ignored it. 'I don't like the houses I provide to be kept in a poor state.'

'Yes, I understand.'

'Good. And there's another point. If she's a nervy, highly-strung neurotic type she'll not be a fit person to be driving Danny to school and home again each day.'

She thought of the narrow, twisting metalled roads

and saw the point. 'I realise what you mean, although I'm still unable to understand why you'd prefer my opinion to Cheryl's. She's older than I am and she's had more experience of life.'

'It's neither your age nor your experience that concerns me, it's your ability to see below the surface, whereas Cheryl can see no further than herself.'

'Oh?' His remark surprised her, causing her to turn to look at him, yet leaving her bereft of further words. Cheryl was fortunate, she decided. Scott knew and understood her faults, yet he loved her despite them. That's if he *did* love her, of course. Suddenly she was unsure about this fact, and with her uncertainty her low spirits began to rise.

They found John and May Roberts waiting for them in a small cottage which, in spite of its age, was spick and span with bulbs blooming in a neatly weeded garden. John, who had been shepherding since leaving school, soon had Scott convinced of his capabilities.

May Roberts poured coffee for them. She was a plump, smiling woman whose quietly spoken remarks indicated good sense. Lindy felt sure that Ellie would approve of her, and it was possible that Scott also realised this fact, because it took little time before arrangements had been made for John to take Eric Briggs' position at Whitecliffs.

It was almost midday when they drove to Waipawa and turned into the supermarket parking-area. Scott handed Ellie's list to Lindy, declaring that he never could find what he wanted among the myriad goods on the shelves. He then pushed the nickel-plated basket trolley between the aisles while Lindy collected items from the shelves.

'This is like pushing a pram,' he remarked with an amused laugh. 'I doubt that you've ever pushed a pram.'

'You do? Then you'd be wrong. Judith and I took

Danny for walks when he was a baby. We took turns to push the pram.'

'It's time you were pushing your own pram,' he remarked in a low voice.

She paused beside the bags of sugar to stare at him. His words had surprised and disturbed her, sending a flush to her cheeks as she sought in her mind for an answer. 'What you're *really* saying is that it's time I went home and found myself a man, got myself married and settled down to domestic life.'

'I did not say that,' he protested.

Her hands shook slightly as she consulted the list, nor was her voice entirely steady as she read aloud, 'Dates, raisins, sultanas, prunes; ah, the dried fruit is along here.'

He indicated the goods already piled in the deep trolley. 'You can see how one must keep track of stores when living in the back country. It's quite beyond some people who are always running short of the things they need.'

Still feeling ruffled, she was quick to imagine hidden meanings behind his words. 'Could that be a warning against marrying Steve?' she demanded coldly. 'I thought you said you realised——'

'That there's nothing between you? Yes, I'm well aware of it. What have I said to upset you to this extent, Lindy? I can see you're really annoyed.'

But to this she could find no reply.

He looked at her critically. 'Something tells me you're in need of a cup of tea. It's time I took you to lunch.'

They pushed the trolley to the check-out counter and then out to the parking-area where they packed the stores into the Citroën. The simple task had a lovely feeling of intimacy about it, and she knew she'd been a fool to have allowed her former irritation to become obvious.

Scott then led her to the tea-room where he ordered a

ham salad lunch, and as she looked about her she recognised the place. 'This is where you brought me on the day of my arrival.'

'Yes, that's right.'

She knew he was watching her closely. 'And now that the day of my departure is almost upon me, here we are again.' She tried to keep her voice light, as if to indicate she didn't care.

'Amazing how the month has flown,' he said in a non-committal tone as he attacked his salad.

She looked at him searchingly. Didn't it matter to him at all? Didn't he care one little scrap that soon she'd be leaving Whitecliffs for ever?

'What's bugging you, Lindy?' The question came abruptly.

Startled, she raked about in her mind for a suitable reply. 'I don't understand.'

'I think you do. You're upset about something and I want to know what it is.'

'It's just that I'll be sorry to leave Whitecliffs,' she admitted miserably. 'I suppose, while I'm in Waipawa I'd better do something about my return bus ticket.'

'Well, actually I wanted to talk to you about that point. Would you object to extending your time with us for another three weeks?'

'*Extending?* No, of course I wouldn't mind.' It was like a reprieve. A weight seemed to be lifted from her, causing her face to brighten and the flecks in her hazel eyes to shine like stars.

CHAPTER NINE

LINDY looked at Scott wonderingly, scarcely daring to believe her ears. He had asked her to extend her time at Whitecliffs, and to make sure she wasn't dreaming she put the question timidly. 'You—you *did* say another three weeks?'

'Yes. Would that be too long?' His tone was casual.

'Oh, no,' she assured him hastily.

'It'll be at least three weeks before May Roberts is settled and ready to drive the boys to school each day. I'd be grateful if you'd stay on until then.'

She was puzzled. 'But won't Cheryl be furious?'

'It's possible.'

'I understood you wanted her to take my place with Danny.'

The dark brows rose. 'Did you hear me say so?'

'No, but Cheryl said——'

'You can forget anything that Cheryl said,' he cut in abruptly. 'Danny is learning very nicely with you, but I do not believe he'd learn as quickly under Cheryl's tuition, because he doesn't like her. It's as simple as that.'

Lindy was surprised. 'Has he said he doesn't like her?'

'No, but I can sense his resentment.'

'I wonder what has caused it.'

'I've no idea. I can only imagine he associates her with his mother, and now Cheryl is there but his mother is not. Who can read what goes on in a child's mind?'

As they drank their tea she became aware that he was regarding her intently. His eyes held her own for several moments, then narrowed slightly as they moved slowly over each feature of her face, resting at last on her lips.

153

She felt her neck go hot, and as her colour deepened she felt the need to ask, 'Is something wrong? Have I a smut on my nose?'

'You're different,' he said unexpectedly.

'I beg your pardon? *Different*?'

'You're not the same person I brought in here on the day of your arrival. You've changed and I've only just realised it.'

'That's ridiculous. How could I possibly change?'

'I don't know, but strangely, you appear to be a little older, almost as if you've suddenly matured. Tell me honestly, have you been happy at Whitecliffs?'

She took a deep breath as the memory of moments in his arms made her eyes shine. 'Oh yes, during these last three weeks there have been times of real joy, moments I'll never forget.'

'But also moments of sadness?' he asked with perception.

She looked down into her cup. 'Yes, that too, but how did you know? Am I so very transparent?'

'Sometimes your eyes tell more than your lips.' He stretched across the table and laid his hand upon hers. His touch had a searing effect which made her long to turn her fingers to clasp his.

'Lindy, forgive me for asking, have you fallen in love?'

The question startled her, and although instinct warned her to remain calm she found herself unable to look at him.

He continued to probe gently. 'Perhaps I've been mistaken, perhaps you've discovered that it's Steve after all?'

'*Steve!*' She snatched her hand away. 'No, it is not,' she gasped in a fury. 'Really, I don't know how you can be so *dumb*. Steve and I have hardly spoken during the last week.'

'I've noticed you appear to be avoiding each other, but now I'm wondering if it's just a lover's tiff.'

'Then you can stop wondering right smartly. Any upset I've had has nothing to do with Steve.'

'In that case am I the culprit? Have I upset you in some way?' The grey eyes became penetrating as they held her own, relentlessly seeking the answer to his questions.

A dull flush began to creep up from her neck as, wordlessly, she returned his gaze. *Had he upset her?* Hadn't he grasped her heart with both hands, twisted it and turned her world topsy-turvy? Her cheeks felt as though they were on fire and her lids began to prickle with a suspicion of tears, causing her to struggle for control of her emotions.

'Can't you tell me, Lindy?' he asked gently.

She shook her head and blinked rapidly, the action enabling her to drag her eyes away from his face. As she did so she became aware that his expression had altered, and he was now looking at her with what appeared to be compassion. The lines about his mouth had softened, and his eyes seemed to be filled with sympathy. Or was it pity?

A sudden horror leapt into her mind. He *knows*, she told herself bitterly. He's guessed I love him, that I'm crazy about him. How could he do otherwise after the way I've responded to his kisses? But to him they meant nothing, and now he's sorry for me.

Acute embarrassment filled her and then pride came to her rescue. Her chin held slightly higher, she slung her shoulder-bag in place. 'If you're ready, shouldn't we be going home?'

'I suppose so, but first I must buy staples for fence repairs.'

'And I'd like to visit the toy-shop. I'm sure Danny would love a humming top, and of course he'll need a school-bag.'

'You appear to be in a hurry. Are you anxious to get back to Whitecliffs, or are you fed up with my probing questions?'

'Let's say a little of both. I fear that your probing questions could be leading your imagination in the wrong direction.' It was a valiant effort to make him think he could be mistaken about any feelings he might think she had for him.

'Is that a fact?' His tone had become gently mocking. 'Well, I trust I won't continue to upset you,' he retorted briefly as they left the tea-room.

The words made her feel desolate, but no doubt it was his way of being cruel to be kind. In other words it was his kindly way of telling her to pull herself together, to snap out of it, to get her emotions back on an even keel and not allow her silly infatuation to be aimed at himself. As Bert had so rightly guessed, Scott didn't wish to become involved with *anyone*.

Lindy forced herself to accept this fact because there was little else she could do about it. Therefore she made a brave effort to show a bright face and to chat amicably during the homeward journey. The miles sped by with surprising speed and it seemed only a short time before the Citroën was parked at the back door, which meant that her day out with Scott was over.

The stores were carried into the kitchen where they found Ellie busily preparing the evening meal while Cheryl sat filing her nails. Scott presented Ellie with a pot-plant of brilliant red cyclamen, and her face beamed at the sight of the flowers.

'They'll help brighten your kitchen,' he told her.

'Oh, thank you, it can do with a spot of brightening at the moment.' She sent him a sly wink.

The grey eyes questioned her. 'Oh? Everything's all right, I trust?' he demanded sharply.

'Well, almost everything,' Ellie said in a resigned voice.

The comment was enough to bring a quick complaint from Cheryl and it needed only a quick glance to see she was in a disgruntled mood. 'It's high time you took

that boy in hand, Scott,' she informed him in an
aggrieved tone.

He turned to frown at her. 'What do you mean? Did
you have trouble in the schoolroom?'

She gave a wild mirthless laugh. '*Trouble in the
schoolroom?* Huh, you can say *that* again. The little imp
wouldn't stay there with me. I can tell you there's been
no school today.' Tears of frustration sprang into her
eyes, causing her to dab at them hastily.

Lindy spoke timidly. 'Did you try reading him a
story?'

'Certainly not,' Cheryl snapped. 'I'm not pandering
to him with stories, nor was a story part of my planned
work.'

At that moment Danny peeped round the edge of the
half-open kitchen door. He saw Lindy and rushed to
fling himself against her. '*She slapped me,*' he wailed
loudly.

'I told you that was a mistake,' Ellie informed
Cheryl.

'He deserved it,' Cheryl snapped angrily. 'He was a
very, *very* naughty boy. He wouldn't do a darned thing
for me. He threw the felt-tip pens on the floor and he
tore the paper. I'm telling you he's a little *brat*.' Fury
now made her voice shake.

Danny began to cry loudly. 'Not a brat, not a
brat——'

Lindy hugged him to her. 'Hush, darling, everything's
all right now,' she consoled him as she wiped the tears
from his eyes. 'Now then, let's have a look among these
parcels. How would you like a nice surprise?' She found
the humming top and set it spinning on the kitchen
floor.

The howls stopped, the tears vanished and Danny's
eyes shone.

'That's right, butter him up to keep yourself the
favourite with him,' Cheryl sneered scathingly.

'That's enough, Cheryl,' Scott snapped. 'A little more buttering on your own part might've been more to the point. In any case his schooldays in the tower are numbered.' He turned to Ellie and told her about John and May Roberts.

A rapid change came over Cheryl's attitude. 'You say it'll be three weeks before she'll begin collecting Danny for school? I'm sure I'll be able to cope with him until then. He'll soon become used to me in the schoolroom instead of Lindy.'

'It won't be necessary,' Scott told her calmly. 'Lindy has agreed to stay here until May Roberts is settled and ready to drive the boys to school.'

Cheryl stared at him almost unbelievingly. 'Are you saying you asked her to do this?'

'Why not? Danny responds to her, as you can see.'

Lindy sighed inwardly. Danny's response to her was Scott's only reason for wanting her to stay for the extra period. There was nothing personal in the request and she could only be thankful for small mercies.

In the tense silence that followed his words Cheryl's face took on an expression of pathos. Her voice quavered slightly as she said, 'What you're *really* saying is that you want me to go home.'

Scott scowled at her. 'I did not say that.'

She moved closer and stood gazing up into his face. 'But you meant it. The promise of this always being my second home is now completely forgotten?' she persisted quietly.

'Of course not,' he muttered, his voice gruff.

'Adrianne always maintained I was part of the family. She'd be so sad, so *unhappy* if she knew you were throwing me out.' She dabbed at her eyes, then pressed her handkerchief to her lips.

He stared at her without speaking.

'Please answer me, Scott, you *are* throwing me out,

aren't you?' The question was accompanied by a whimper.

His voice became hard. 'Not yet, but who knows? The time might come. Now go and remove those mascara smudges. They look awful.'

She brightened visibly. 'Thank you, darling, I knew I could rely on your memory. You couldn't possibly forget all we've been to each other over the years.'

'Really? What, exactly, have we been to each other over the years, Cheryl?'

'Well, you know, like brother and sister.' She reached up and kissed his cheek, then left the room with a smiling little side glance at Lindy.

However, it took time for Cheryl to completely regain her confidence and she was still subdued during dinner. Her usual slightly forced gay chatter was missing, and she sat wrapped in an air of injured pride.

If Scott noticed her attitude he ignored it while telling Steve about John Roberts.

Steve said, 'As soon as he's settled I'll take another trip to Wellington. I'll get it in before the worst of the lambing is upon us.' He turned to Lindy. 'Would you like to be driven home? Considering I arranged for you to come here it seems only right that I arrange for your return journey.'

Lindy was startled but tried not to show it. 'Thank you, but there's no need,' she told him hastily. 'I'll be quite happy in the bus, even if it does take a little longer.'

He shrugged as though to indicate he couldn't care less about which way she went home. 'Very well, have it your own way,' he retorted briefly, then turned to Scott to continue with a further question concerning the Robertses. 'I presume you discussed driving Danny to school with Mrs Roberts?'

'Yes. She's delighted to know there's another small boy here,' Scott said. 'Especially one near her own son's age.'

'They'll probably fight,' Cheryl prophesied irritably. 'There will be trouble, just you wait and see.'

'Snap out of it, Cheryl,' Scott advised curtly.

Lindy regarded her curiously. The subject of the Robertses seemed to depress Cheryl, no doubt because it spelt the end of her aspirations to take over after Lindy's departure.

A diversion then occurred when Danny came running into the room. He stood beside Lindy's chair, his blue eyes round and serious as he gazed up at her. 'Bert says you're wrong about those sheep,' he declared almost accusingly.

She was puzzled. 'Sheep? What sheep? I'm afraid I don't understand what you mean, dear.'

He gave an impatient hop. 'You know, those sheep in the field. If there are ten sheep in a field and one gets out there'd be nine left.'

'Oh, *those* sheep.'

'Bert says you're wrong. Bert says if there are ten sheep in a field and one gets out, the whole dratted lot would get out. There'd be *none* left.'

Everybody laughed and the atmosphere became lighter.

'Of course Bert's right,' Steve agreed.

Even Cheryl became less tense but was unable to resist throwing a pointed remark at Lindy. 'You know so little, so *very* little about what happens on a farm.'

Scott caught the sneer behind her words. He sent Cheryl a level glance as he said, 'That remark was entirely uncalled-for, Cheryl. Is this your way of showing friendship towards Lindy?'

Cheryl's tone changed at once. 'Really, Scott, we're the best of friends, aren't we, Lindy?' There was an appeal for confirmation in her voice.

Lindy longed to say that Cheryl could have fooled her, but she merely smiled and said nothing. Nor was her silence lost on Scott, whose eyes narrowed slightly as he looked from one to the other.

Later he drew Lindy aside to the privacy of his office where he questioned her quietly. His face was serious as he asked, 'Is it true? Relations between you and Cheryl have really improved? I noticed you did not agree with her, nor did you agree when she made a similar statement earlier today.'

Lindy looked away, avoiding his eyes. 'She has said so, hasn't she?'

'But what do *you* say? I want the truth.'

'I suppose you could say we tolerate each other, although you must be able to see that my presence in this house makes her most unhappy. She's longing for me to leave.'

'What about you? Does her presence here make you unhappy?'

She drew a sharp breath. 'Scott, this is a ridiculous conversation. Her presence is not my concern, but it obviously makes *you* happy, otherwise you wouldn't persist in her remaining here.' Then before she could stop herself she added bitterly, 'Why don't you ask her to marry you and be done with it?'

'Do I act as though I'm in love with her?'

Lindy paused to consider his attitude towards Cheryl. 'No. To be honest, I don't think you do,' she admitted at last.

'Then it was a stupid question, wasn't it?'

'I suppose so. Nor is it my business. Sorry I asked.'

'Let me assure you that never in my life have I had any intention of marrying Cheryl. Didn't you hear her admit to a brother-and-sister relationship? It's never been any closer than that. Do you understand?'

The urgency behind the question surprised her. 'Yes. What I *don't* understand is why you're so anxious to impress these facts upon me.' She looked at him expectantly.

'Because for some damned stupid reason that escapes me, I'd prefer you to be aware of the true situation between Cheryl and myself.'

His words caused her pulses to quicken, and her eyes shone as rays of hope flashed into her mind. He *cared* about what she thought? It was difficult to believe.

He went on to explain. 'Through Adrianne this place has become like a second home to Cheryl, and *because* of Adrianne it would take something mighty big to make me terminate her visits.'

'Oh, I see.' Her spirits returned to zero. 'Well, as my own visit terminates as soon as May Roberts is ready to drive Danny to school, I can't see why you should worry about what I think about the situation between Cheryl and yourself.'

'You can't see any reason at all?' His eyes seemed to bore into her mind as though sifting her thoughts to examine them one by one.

'If you're expecting an answer to that question I'm afraid I haven't one,' she managed to say coolly. 'Isn't it time we returned to the lounge?'

'Perhaps you're right.' His tone was suddenly abrupt as he stood aside to allow her to precede him through the door.

There was no attempt to detain her or to extend their time alone, she noticed sadly. And then her attention was caught by Danny who met them in the hall.

'Ellie says the sun might shine tomorrow. Ellie says red sky at night, shepherd's delight. Does that mean fine weather?'

'You've got something on your mind, old chap?' Scott drawled.

'If the sun shines can we fly my kite?'

'I'm afraid Uncle Steve and I will be busy tomorrow. We'll be deciding which of the deer are to be sold.'

'I'll fly it with him,' Lindy offered. 'I promised there'd be kite-flying when the sun shone, and you know the rule about never breaking one's promise to a child.'

He looked at her doubtfully. 'Do you think you can manage to get it up?'

'I can only do my best.'

'You can't go down to the riverflats because they're almost under water, but you could possibly get it aloft on the plateau paddock in front of the house. The water doesn't lie there as it does down on the riverflats.' He glanced down at the boy. 'You'll make sure a certain party doesn't investigate the crevice in the cliffs?'

'Of course. He'll be too busy holding his kite,' she smiled.

Ellie's prophecy for better weather proved to be correct as the next morning found the sun shining between white clouds that scudded across large patches of blue sky. And instead of being driven by a bitterly cold wind from the snow-topped ranges they wafted along on an easterly breeze which promised to lift the kite to a good height.

Discipline demanded that the usual school lessons took place in the morning, but as soon as lunch was finished Lindy and Danny made their way towards the front paddock. They had almost reached the gate when Danny stopped suddenly. 'Ted,' he said. 'Ted wants to come too.' And without another word he raced back to the house.

Lindy stood and waited for him, smiling to herself as she realised Ted had been forgotten. School lessons appeared to be opening Danny's mind to wider horizons, and Ted was beginning to take a back seat. The time was not far distant when he'd be placed in the toy-cupboard and left there.

A few minutes later, with Ted lightly clutched in his hand, they made their way into the paddock. Sheep scattered to the far end, and as the breeze freshened Lindy ran with the kite. The string slid through her fingers as the red and yellow bird soared aloft with its spread of tail floating behind.

Danny dropped Ted near the fence, then ran behind her shouting with excitement. 'Let me hold it, I wanna hold it, let me fly my kite.'

She handed the bar holder to him, then stood to watch his utter joy as he gazed upward. The air was fresh but not too cold, and the breeze blew Lindy's light brown hair about her face.

Slowly they made their way from one end of the paddock to the other, and they were near a gate when the sight of Cheryl crossing the front lawn caused Lindy to pause, surprised that she should wish to join them.

But Cheryl was not interested in kite-flying. Instead she had come with a message for Lindy. 'Your mother phoned,' she informed her as she came through the gate. 'I told her you'd ring her when you came in.'

Lindy felt a spasm of alarm, her mind darting between sickness or accident that could have struck one of her parents. 'Did she say why she was ringing me? Is something wrong?'

Cheryl gave a slight shrug. 'How would I know?' She paused before adding casually, 'I must say I thought she sounded worried.'

Lindy's fears rose. 'Perhaps I'd better go in and ring her at once.' She turned to Danny. 'I'm afraid we'll have to wind the kite down now, dear.'

But Danny protested loudly. 'No, no,' he shrieked, giving small stamps of fury. 'Not going inside, I want to fly my kite. You said we'd fly my kite, *you promised*.' The tears fell.

Lindy sent Cheryl a look of helplessness. 'He's been waiting for a fine day for ages.'

'Okay, I'll stay with him while you go and ring your mother. Perhaps she's ringing for you to go home at once, perhaps somebody's ill.' Despite the latter unhappy thought Cheryl's voice held a tinge of hope.

Lindy slipped through the gate and hurried across the lawn to the house. The front door had been left open by Cheryl, so she was able to reach the hall phone quickly, and within moments she heard the receiver lifted in the lounge at home.

'Is everything all right?' she asked anxiously when the familiar voice of her mother came over the line.

'Yes, of course, dear.'

'Cheryl said you sounded worried.'

'I only wanted to know if everything was all right with *you*. Apart from that first letter I haven't heard a word from you. Your father and I were beginning to wonder how you're getting along with the people in that place.'

'Everything's fine, Mother.' It wasn't, but how could she tell her mother otherwise? How could she go into details concerning her love for Scott? Her mother's voice came again.

'How are you managing with the little boy? It's all so foreign to you, I've wondered about you every day.'

'We're getting along nicely, he's really quite smart.'

'Judith says you haven't answered her letter. She keeps coming in from next door to ask if I've heard from you. I think she's feeling a little hurt. Are you so busy you're unable to write even a few lines?'

Lindy was consumed with guilt. Her mother was right. Her letter-writing had been neglected, but how could she put pen to paper when most of her thoughts were being affected by Scott Wardell? Something of her state of mind would slip between the lines, she felt sure.

She said, 'I'm sorry, Mother. I should've written before this, but I'll be home in about three weeks.'

'Home?' Her mother's voice echoed surprise. 'Is your teaching job finished? Have you found it too difficult? I can't help feeling that something's wrong.'

'There is nothing wrong,' Lindy assured her patiently. 'It's just that other arrangements have been made. I'll

write and tell you about them, that's a promise.
Goodbye. Give Daddy my love.'

She replaced the receiver, then turned to see Scott
regarding her from the doorway of his office. 'I owe
you for a call to Wellington,' she explained. 'I had to
ring my mother.'

'To tell her you'd be home in three weeks? Are you so
anxious to leave this place?'

'Of course not, but what other option is there for me?'

'There *could* be another option if you're interested,
and if you're sure you're not hankering for the city
lights.'

Her breath quickened. 'What do you mean?'

'It's possible I could find you another job.' He raised
his hand to gently stroke her cheek, his touch having a
searing effect that sent colour flying into her face.

She stared up at him wide-eyed. 'I don't understand.'

He came a step closer, his head bent slightly as he
scanned her features. 'Did you know you have lights in
your eyes? Sometimes they glow like flecks of gold.
Have you ever seen the specks of gold in a miner's pan?'
His deep voice was low.

She shook her head in a bemused manner.

'But you must know you're quite beautiful.'

Her colour deepened. 'Thank you. It's not something
I think about.' Her pulses raced as she found joy in the
fact that he considered her to be nice to look at. Then,
not allowing his compliment to go to her head she said,
'This—this other job you mentioned. Isn't it something
Cheryl could do?'

He gave a short laugh. 'I doubt that she'd fit in at all.
It needs a very special person.'

'Oh? What sort of person?' She was puzzled by the
enigmatic expression on his face as his gaze held her
own. At the same time it made her heart thump and she
knew she had to get at his meaning. 'What sort of
person?' she repeated.

'One who has been hand-picked for the job,' he replied softly. 'Something tells me you could do it nicely.'

'I'm intrigued. Tell me more,' she encouraged.

'This is neither the time nor the place,' he retorted coolly. 'Will you listen when the time comes?'

'Of course. But surely you can tell me about the job now?'

But before he could say more the sound of approaching voices struck a discordant note, and, frustrated, she knew the moment was lost as Cheryl and Danny came in through the front door. The little boy carried the kite while Cheryl managed the bunch of long tail.

Danny was tearful. 'Cheryl said we had to come inside,' he complained in a grizzling whine.

'There were spits of rain,' she reminded him brightly and without disguising the fact that this had been a godsend. And then her green eyes narrowed as they regarded the slight flush still clinging to Lindy's cheeks. 'Are we interrupting something?' she demanded abruptly, her tone full of suspicion.

'Nothing important,' Scott assured her smoothly.

Lindy sent him a quick glance as she felt the dull ache of depression seeping into her mind. *Nothing important*, he'd said. Was this his way of letting her know he couldn't care less whether or not she accepted the job he'd referred to? And then she became aware that he was speaking to Danny.

'There'll be plenty of other days for kite-flying, old chap,' he promised as he glanced at his watch. 'Do you know that other boys are still in the classroom? I think you have time to count a few more sheep or green bottles before school ends for the day.'

Lindy took the hint and led Danny upstairs, but on reaching the tower she found him to be most unwilling to put his mind to lessons. Compromise was necessary, therefore she read him the story of the Little Red Hen which was skilfully followed by an exercise in counting eggs and printing associated words such as nest, barn, red, hen and eggs.

But if Danny's thoughts were still with his kite Lindy's own concentration was little better because Scott's face kept hovering before her mind, while the question of the job he'd mentioned swam round in her brain.

But to what job did he refer? The only one she could think of would entail helping Ellie in the running of the house, and then revelation struck in a blinding flash as the whole situation became as clear as a bright light on a dark night. All he wanted was a *servant* in the house, an assistant for Ellie who, after all, was no longer as young as she used to be.

But surely this would not need a special person who had been hand-picked? Yet in a way it did because the job required someone who would suit Ellie. Hadn't Scott considered Ellie from the very beginning? Lindy recalled his objections to herself on the day of her arrival.

Nor would Cheryl be a suitable help for Ellie, because there was little love lost between them. As Scott had declared, she would not fit in. In any case the job would not suit Cheryl, who would look upon it as being menial and well beneath her own personal aspirations which were to become the mistress of Whitecliffs rather than the maid in the kitchen. A smile touched Lindy's lips as she visualised Cheryl's wrathful reaction to such a suggestion.

Housework? Me? You've got to be joking.

But what of her own reactions to the situation? For a moment her chin rose in defiant pride, then just as quickly it sank down to her chest as she realised that no matter what type of job was offered, she'd accept it.

At least it would enable her to remain at Whitecliffs, and it would keep her close to Scott. The thought of leaving Whitecliffs, and of never seeing Scott again, almost brought a small gasp of pain to her lips.

CHAPTER TEN

WHEN school was finished for the day Lindy went to her room and wrote letters to her mother and to Judith Hunter. And although she told them about Mrs Roberts and the approaching end of the schoolteaching situation, she made no mention of a future job having been offered.

The thought of it sent her to the kitchen to see if there was anything she could do to help Ellie with the evening meal, but there was nothing. Ellie, as efficient as ever, had everything under control, and Lindy began to wonder why Scott was so anxious to find assistance for her.

To put the question to the test she asked gently, 'What would you say to an extra pair of hands about the place?'

Ellie sent her a sharp glance. 'Whose hands, might I ask?'

'Oh, anyone's,' Lindy prevaricated. 'Perhaps mine, or Cheryl's.'

'*Cheryl's?* Huh! That'll be the day. As for yours, you'd do better to keep them for something more interesting than housework, because I certainly don't need them.'

'But you've so much to do, Ellie.'

'That's true, but you'd be surprised by the amount of help Bert gives me, and I've only to ring Jake Lomas's wife for extra assistance like cleaning windows.' She sent Lindy a shrewd glance. 'What's brought this on? What made you ask such a question?'

Lindy found difficulty in finding an answer. 'Oh, Scott said something about a job for me here, I mean when Danny is being driven to school. I presumed it'd be to help you.'

'*Me?* It's more likely to be one that'll help him,' Ellie said thoughtfully.

'What do you mean?' Lindy's voice was alive with interest.

'An office job. You can type, I suppose, and as you've worked for an accountant you're sure to be good with figures. Scott has trouble in keeping his accounts, and when he wants to be outside he becomes frustrated by having to do the farm clerical work.'

'Isn't it a job that Cheryl could do?' Lindy asked carefully.

Ellie sniffed with a hint of disdain. 'One presumes she could do it. Adrianne often helped him but I've never known Cheryl to do so. Perhaps he never asked her.'

'And perhaps it's not what he has in mind,' Lindy pointed out. 'I'll just have to wait until he tells me about it.'

But although Lindy waited expectantly during the period of their pre-dinner drinks Scott made no further mention of any job that would cause her to remain at Whitecliffs. Nor was the subject brought up during dinner, when the conversation was dominated by details concerning the coming deer sale to be held on the property.

There was one mad moment when she almost broached the subject herself, and it was only Steve's voice listing the important buyers who were at last year's sale that kept her silent. She was then grateful that the impulse had been curbed, and vowed she would wait until Scott himself mentioned it to her.

Later, when they were about to settle in the lounge, Lindy remembered the letters she had written earlier. They were still in her room and she knew they must be left on the hall table from where they would be collected for the mail bag; therefore she left the lounge and went along the passage, but as she passed Danny's bedroom she was brought to an abrupt halt by the sound of sobbing.

Peeping into the room she discovered the small boy sitting up in bed, his eyes streaming, his face red from weeping. She crossed the room quickly and put her arms about him. Holding him closely she exclaimed, 'Danny dear, what's the matter?'

'Ted, I want Ted,' he gasped as the tears fell afresh.

'Ted came with us to fly the kite,' she reminded him, her thoughts sweeping back to his return to the house for the bear. Ted was a real person and had to be referred to as such. 'Didn't you bring him inside when you came in with Cheryl?'

He shook his head, gazing at her through more tears. 'He's out in the dark, he'll get wet if it rains.'

Scott's deep voice spoke from the doorway. 'What's the matter? No, don't tell me, let me guess. Ted's gone walkabout.'

Her heart almost turned over as she gazed up at his handsome face. 'I'm afraid he's been left outside. Have you a torch? I don't think it would take too long to find him.' She went on to explain how, in the excitement of flying the kite, Ted must have been dropped, and she then added, 'When Cheryl took over while I went to the phone she didn't realise that Ted had been with us, or had been dropped.'

'I see. Right. I'll get a torch and we'll go out together. You'll need stronger shoes and a coat.'

Lindy wiped Danny's eyes. 'We'll go and find Ted,' she promised. 'Be a good boy and stop crying.' She tucked the blankets round him, then went to her room. Moments later she met Scott in the passage.

Cheryl came into the hall as he opened the front door. 'Where on earth are you going?' she demanded suspiciously, her eyes taking in Lindy's jacket and heavy shoes. 'A moonlight stroll, is it? So why the torch?'

'We're going out to find Ted,' Scott told her curtly. 'He's somewhere out in the front paddock.'

'I'll come too,' she offered quickly.

'There's no need to make it a search party,' he told her in a bland tone as he ushered Lindy out through the door, then closed it after them.

His hand was tucked beneath her arm as they followed the bright beam of the torch down the wide concrete steps, and as they walked along the drive his fingers slid down her jacket sleeve to clasp her own in a firm grip.

A heady perfume came from the nearby garden, causing her to pause and draw in a deep breath. 'The daphne's in bloom,' she remarked, making an effort to control a vocal tremor caused by his touch.

'Yes. Ellie waits all the year for it to blossom. Any day now she'll have small bowls of it dotted about the house.'

'It's beautiful.' As she took another deep breath she became conscious that the night had an air of romance about it. Above them the black velvet canopy of sky had been swept clear of clouds and was now pricked by countless stars.

But Scott did not appear to be aware of anything in the way of a romantic atmosphere when he said abruptly, 'There are a couple of gates into the paddock. Which one did you go through?'

'The one on the western end. We crossed the lawn to it, but I don't think Ted was dropped until we were getting the kite aloft. The wind was from the east,' she added, describing the way they had moved across the paddock.

He did not release her hand until it was necessary to open the gate, and then the torch was swung from left to right. Sheep were disturbed and scrambled to their feet, their eyes shining like green diamonds as they reflected the beams of light. But one diamond did not run away, and closer inspected proved it to be Ted's glassy eye.

Lindy snatched him up, then breathed a sigh of relief when the torchlight revealed him to be still clean and in good order, even if a little damp from falling dew.

Scott said, 'He's lucky he hasn't been trampled by sheep.'

As they turned to retrace their steps a muffled roar caught Lindy's ears, and, pausing to listen she said, 'Is that the river? It sounds very loud.

'Yes. Whether high or low the sound comes up through the crevice. Remember the story of the Maori warriors whose voices were heard by the sentry above?'

The thought made her quake inwardly. 'Thank heavens a sentry is no longer necessary.'

He led her towards the sound, and when she almost stumbled on a patch of rough ground he took a firm grip on the arm that was not clutching Ted. It gave her a glow of comfort, making her grateful for his support, while the happiness that engulfed her made her feel that these moments were unreal.

The torch sent a beam towards the cliff fence, and as they reached it she saw the wide black gaping hole. The sight of it made her draw back instinctively. 'It looks so eerie at night,' she said nervously. 'Like a bottomless pit.'

'Don't be afraid, it's only a crevice.' His arm went about her protectively. 'It's difficult to scramble up or down in winter. It suffers from eroson and the rains make the soil slip. If you step too near the edge after a long period of heavy rain you're in danger of feeling the ground collapse beneath your feet.'

'Which means you'd find yourself slithering down to the river?' It was an effort to keep her voice steady, not because of fear but because of his nearness which seemed to unhinge her.

'That's right. You'd then be swept along by a raging torrent of muddy water. Not a nice experience, especially if you're thrown against the bottom of the cliffs or hit by floating logs.'

She moved closer to him. 'The thought gives me the horrors.'

'And there's something else to be watched. During very wet winters the top edge of the crevice creeps a little closer to the fence, and when this happens the fence has to be brought back a short distance, otherwise there'll be a gap beneath it.'

'And then the sheep will decide that the grass is sweeter on the other side,' she supplied with understanding. 'Any that push their way beneath it could land in the river. As Bert said, if one gets out, they'll all get out.'

He laughed. 'Right. You're catching on to the habits of sheep quite smartly. How would you like to be a farmer's wife?'

She drew a sharp breath, then looked at him in a dazed way. Surely, this couldn't be a proposal of marriage, she thought wildly. No, of course it wasn't. It was merely a casual question and she was being a fool to imagine it to be anything else. 'I hadn't thought about it,' she lied, then lapsed into silence as she waited for him to say more.

But before he could do so a muffled plop came to their ears as a large clod of earth fell from the cliffs. 'It's a horrible crevice,' she exclaimed vehemently.

As though sensing her fear he held her closer, both arms now enfolding her while one hand pressed her head against his shoulder.

A surge of excitement sent her pulses pounding as she waited for him to lower his own head and find her lips, but he seemed to be lost in thought as he gazed towards the long line of cliff edge.

'You'll be safe while you stay on this side of the fence,' was all he said.

'I'll do that,' she assured him, then tentatively raised her face as the silver moon sailed from behind a cloud to lighten the surrounding darkness and glow on her features.

He looked down at her, his eyes shadowed. 'By moonlight you're bewitching. You're like a beautiful madonna,' he murmured in a low voice.

She returned his gaze in silence, her face still uplifted, but while she knew she was blatantly inviting his kiss she was past caring about this fact. And then her heart leapt as he slowly lowered his head to trail his lips lightly across her brow and cheek.

She closed her eyes, waiting for the pressure of his lips on her own, but when it did not come she looked up to find him gazing at her with an unfathomable expression that not even the semi-darkness of the moonlight could conceal. It left her feeling puzzled, but overriding this was the frustrated longing for the kiss that had failed to eventuate. *Why hadn't he kissed her?*

In an effort to hide her deep disappointment she said, 'Danny will be wondering if we've found Ted. I'm surprised he hasn't come out to help search for him.'

'He knows he was told to stay in bed. For a small boy he's fairly well disciplined,' Scott said with a hint of satisfaction.

'Discipline is such a stern word, especially when applied to a small boy,' she protested.

'It can also be applied to a big boy,' he retorted grimly as they turned to retrace their steps across the field.

Surprised, she sent him a quick glance. 'One would almost imagine you're referring to yourself.'

'Of course. Who else?'

She was even more surprised. 'Are you saying you've failed to discipline *yourself*?'

'Yes. I've failed miserably.'

She was curious. 'In what way have you failed?'

'Just let it be said that I've failed. My discipline has flown on the wind.'

She fell silent, trying to fathom his meaning yet fearing a rebuff if she probed further. 'I don't understand,' she admitted at last.

'No, I don't suppose you do.' Nor did he enlighten her, and they went through the gate in silence.

As they crossed the lawn her mind was gripped by memory of the job he had offered to her. Should she bring up the subject, or should she leave it for him to do so? These moments alone in the moonlight presented a golden opportunity to discuss private matters, so she said, 'You mentioned a job I could fill. Can you tell me about it?'

He was silent until they stepped from the lawn to the drive, then, as though having considered the question, he paused beside the heavily perfumed daphne bush growing in the garden beneath the lounge windows. 'Now is not the right moment,' he said at last.

'Not even the slightest hint?'

'You'll consider anything I offer?'

'Of course. Please tell me.'

His answer was to turn her to face him, and she looked up at him intently, trying to read the enigmatic expression on his face. His strong hands took possession of her body, pressing her against the length of his own with an intimacy that sent spasms of desire shooting through her veins.

Firm fingers tilted her chin while he kissed her brow, her lids and then her lips, gently at first, then teasingly until she almost quivered and moaned with longing. Her arms clung to him fiercely while she gave herself up to the joy of these moments which were wafting her up into a haze of ecstasy.

The mounting of his own passion caused him to kiss her as deeply as she had yearned to be kissed when they had been out in the field. Nor was she unaware of the silent message, the calling of his body that told her he ached to make love to her, and, loving him as she did, she knew that if the circumstances had allowed she would have succumbed to his demands by giving herself to him.

When his lips left hers in a momentary pause she was unable to resist a whispered question. 'Why didn't you kiss me like this out there?'

His voice was low. 'Don't you understand? If I had I doubt that we'd have returned to the house for hours.'

'Would it have mattered?' she asked with great daring.

'You're forgetting Ted. And we'd have had not only Danny but the rest of the household out in a search party.'

'Yes, of course. I'm a stupid idiot.'

'But a most delightful one.'

She looked at him in pained silence. Delightful? Was that all? Had he not yet reached the stage when his feelings for her went beyond casual kisses? Apparently not.

Disappointed, she turned her head away, pressing her cheek against his shoulder. Her eyes were wide as they stared unseeingly at the wall beyond the garden and she thought about his remark. She'd make a delightful companion, no doubt, but nothing more. And then her attention was caught by the movement of a sliver of light that fell across the waxy rose-pink flowers of the daphne bush. It came from between the lounge curtains, and, looking up, she caught a brief glimpse of Cheryl's red hair.

She drew a sharp breath then said nervously, 'I'm not sure, but I *think* Cheryl has been watching us through the window.'

'She has?'

'The bright moonlight will have shown her everything so clearly.'

'Everything? There's been very little to see.'

'Perhaps we should go inside,' she quavered.

'Unnerves you, does she?'

'Definitely. And there's also the question of Ted.'

'Are you sure she *did* see us?'

'No, I'm not sure. It was just that I thought I caught a quick flash of red hair, but to be honest I can't be positive. At the same time I *think* the curtain moved.'

'Well, if you can't be sure we'll just have to hope for the best,' he said, brushing the matter aside as though it didn't matter, and it was this fact that made her feel more cheerful.

When they went inside Ted was wrapped in a towel because of his slight dampness. He was then delivered to a grateful Danny who cuddled him down into the bed and promised to go to sleep.

Scott went to the lounge, but Lindy made a hasty visit to her bedroom where she pressed a cold wet face-cloth to her burning cheeks and renewed her make-up. When she entered the lounge Scott and Steve were already engrossed in a discussion concerning the fence near the crevice.

Cheryl sent her a cool smile which failed to reach her eyes. 'You took a long time to find Ted,' she remarked.

'Oh, not really,' Lindy informed her casually. 'Most of the time was spent near the crevice, as you'll hear if you listen to what Scott is saying about the fence.' Had Cheryl peeped through the curtains to observe their embrace? she wondered.

She knew it was possible, but it was also equally possible that she had not. Only time would tell, because Cheryl was unlikely to allow such an incident to pass without comment. And then she realised that Cheryl was carefully examining every inch of her face, particularly her lips. Was there a swelling or trace of Scott's ardent kisses? Thank heavens she'd renewed her make-up, or was it this fact alone that had brought the glint of suspicion into the green eyes?

But strangely, and to Lindy's surprise, Cheryl's attitude took on a note of unexpected friendliness which enabled them to spend the rest of the evening chatting amicably. The relief was immense, and by the time she went to bed Lindy felt secure in the belief that Cheryl had not peeped through the curtains to watch Scott holding her in his arms.

The improved relations between them continued during the next few days, although Lindy's schoolteaching hours in the tower forbade that they spent much time together. However, she did notice that, despite the spell of fine weather, Cheryl was no longer riding out each day with Scott. Nor was the subject of horseriding mentioned until the following Saturday morning at breakfast, when it was brought up by Scott, who turned to Cheryl and said, 'Correct me if I'm mistaken, but didn't you promise to give Lindy riding-lessons?'

Cheryl was startled. 'Yes, I—er—did say something about it.'

'How is she coming along?' Steve asked smoothly.

Cheryl's mouth tightened. 'We haven't actually got started yet,' she admitted, avoiding his eyes.

'Are you saying you haven't had her up on old Meg?' Scott demanded. 'It was mentioned ages ago.'

'That's right.' Cheryl glared at him defiantly.

Scott's voice hardened. 'So when do you intend to begin?'

Cheryl became sulky. 'There's not much point, is there?' She'll be leaving as soon as Mrs Roberts begins driving Danny to school.'

'A promise is a promise.' Scott's voice was still hard.

Cheryl turned to glance at the wintry sun streaming across the lawn beyond the window. 'Oh, well, I suppose I could give her a short turn this morning,' she conceded reluctantly.

Lindy had heard enough of the discussion. 'Thanks, you needn't bother,' she exclaimed wrathfully. 'Nor does it amuse me to be discussed as though I'm not here.' She felt bitterly disappointed. Was this the same Cheryl who had been so friendly during the week? She might've known it was only a veneer. 'If you really don't wish to give me a riding-lesson I couldn't care less,' she added with her chin raised.

Cheryl's manner changed suddenly. 'Oh, but I *do* want to give you lessons,' she assured Lindy. 'I *promised*, didn't I? It's just that I hadn't got round to it.'

'Start her off on a sheepskin,' Steve advised. 'It'll help teach her to grip with her knees.'

'I know what to do,' Cheryl snapped crossly.

'Would you like me to catch Meg for you?' he offered.

She looked at him loftily. 'Steve, you should know by now that Meg comes right up to me.'

'Ah yes, but that's because she knows you've got lumps of sugar in your hand,' he teased.

'You're right,' she admitted. 'I'll see if Ellie can let me have some.' She left the table and went to find Ellie who was busy in the pantry.

As she did so Danny came to stand beside Scott's chair. The little boy's eyes were anxious as he looked up pleadingly. 'Uncle Scott, could you fix the roof of my farm woolshed? It's broken.'

'I'm afraid the front gable has come adrift,' Lindy hastened to explain. 'Have you a glue that will hold plastic together?'

Scott put his arm round the boy in a kindly manner. 'Okay, old chap, we'll see what can be done about it. Not every glue will hold plastic, but I might have a suitable one. I'll take it up to the tower after breakfast.'

'Thank you, Uncle Scott,' Danny beamed.

A few minutes later Cheryl returned to the table with

several lumps of sugar which she showed to Lindy.
'Lesson number one, here we have the secret of catching
a horse.'

A short time later they put on warm jackets and
made their way to a stable situated on the edge of a
paddock where several horses were grazing. The grey
mare raised her head to watch their approach and as
Cheryl called to her she came forward slowly.

'You see? She knows I have sugar,' Cheryl said
tightly as though controlling an inner irritation.

Lindy looked at her curiously. It needed little
imagination to guess that Cheryl had no wish to give
her this riding-lesson, but she ignored the angry tone
and watched as a bridle was taken from the wall. She
observed Cheryl's swift and expert movements as it was
placed on the mare's head, but noticed that no
explanation of the procedure was offered.

'Hold her,' Cheryl ordered petulantly handing over
the reins, and again her resentment came through loud
and clear.

A soft woolly sheepskin was taken from the stable
and secured to Meg's back by a surcingle, and the mare
was then led to a stump which enabled Lindy to mount.
Her cheeks became flushed as exhilaration coupled with
a sense of excitement gripped her, but this was soon
crushed by Cheryl's attitude which appeared to be
growing more cross every moment.

And then she noticed that Cheryl carried a stockwhip
in her hand. 'What's that for?' she asked with a sudden
feeling of apprehension. 'I hope you don't expect me to
use it.'

Cheryl shrugged. 'It's just a precaution,' she said
nonchalantly. 'Meg will behave if she knows it's
around.'

'It appears to be a really punishing weapon,' Lindy
remarked without realising the truth of her observation.

'You can say that again,' Cheryl retorted grimly. 'It's

a top-quality Australian whip with a tough six-foot thong of plaited kangaroo hide.' She led the mare through the gate towards the drive, and with the animal stepping quietly they passed the front steps.

Lindy's lighter spirits had begun to return and as they came to the daphne shrub she drew in a deep breath. 'Isn't it a heavenly perfume? I'll always remember this particular bush.'

'I'll bet you will,' Cheryl flashed at her with a burst of uncontrolled fury. 'It's where Scott kissed you, isn't it? Don't imagine I didn't see you, *because I did*. Didn't I warn you to keep your hands off him?'

Lindy was shocked by the outburst, and, sitting on Meg's back, she was unable to find a reply as she looked down into Cheryl's angry face. So, Cheryl *had* seen them after all, she realised as they crossed the lawn towards the gate leading into the front house paddock, but what could she say? Perhaps it would be better to ignore the remark and in an effort to change the subject she looked back over her shoulder and said, 'Should we have come this way? Meg's hoofs have made awful holes in the lawn.'

Cheryl stood still and looked back at the indentations made in the soft turf, but instead of giving them only a brief glance Lindy noticed that her eyes also scanned the windows of the house. 'Poof, who cares?' she snapped at last. 'Bert will soon fill them in.' She then led Meg through the gate and closed it after her.

For some reason of her own Meg quickened her steps, making her way towards the cliff fence. But Lindy had no wish to go in that direction and was doing her best to pull the mare's head round when an eruption of Cheryl's rage exploded over her.

No doubt it had been simmering for some time, but it had now reached boiling point as the long thong of the whip whirled in the air. 'I'll teach you to ride,' she yelled. 'I'll teach you to steal my man. *Take that, and that.*'

The vicious blows from the whip fell across Lindy's back, which was fortunately protected by her warm jacket, and across Meg's hindquarters which were not protected. The first caused Lindy to scream from shock as the mare reared from the unexpected lash from the whip, while the second attack sent Meg bolting across the field with Lindy lying along her back while she clung desperately to the grey neck and mane. She knew they were moving towards the crevice and she screamed again, her eyes wide with terror as she feared Meg might jump the fence and take them over the cliffs to the river.

But at the fence Meg swerved to the right while Lindy kept going straight ahead, flying over the wires to land spreadeagled on the grass only a yard from the crevice. The wind was completely knocked out of her, while the shock sent her into a daze where vague thoughts drifted hazily through her mind.

Was the ground about to give way beneath her? Had she suffered any broken bones in the fall? She was afraid to move her limbs in an effort to find out, so she continued to lie still, her eyes closed as she listened to the sound of the river coming up the crevice.

Above the sound of the river she could hear Cheryl's voice quavering nervously from the other side of the fence. 'Are you all right? *Lindy*, can you hear me? For God's sake, *say something*. You've got to learn to fall off a horse.'

But Lindy remained silent, her eyes still closed, and feeling too exhausted and stunned to make the effort to answer Cheryl. And then her ears caught the sound of a shout which was followed by a tremulous exclamation from Cheryl.

'Oh hell, Scott's on his way. Now there'll be one heck of a fuss. For Pete's sake get up, Lindy, you *can't* be badly hurt.'

By that time the discomfort of lying face downwards

on the cold wet grass was beginning to make Lindy aware of the necessity to test her limbs, but for some strange reason Cheryl's words delayed the action. She continued to lie still, and moments later there was a creaking of wires as Scott climbed over the fence. She knew that he knelt beside her, and as she felt the gentle touch of his hands examining her arms and legs new life seemed to surge through her.

His voice vibrated with anxiety. 'Darling, can you hear me?'

Darling? It was beyond her to remain silent. 'Yes.'

'Are you hurting anywhere in particular?'

'No, just one big ache all over. I suppose I've been jarred.'

'Let's get you to your feet.' He lifted her up and she leaned against him while his arms supported her.

The action was enough to bring a scathing comment from Cheryl. 'I *knew* she was really all right.'

Scott turned upon her in a fury. 'And damned lucky for you that she is. What the hell got into you?'

'What do you mean?' Cheryl demanded defiantly.

'Don't try to bluff it out with me, you spitfire,' he raged. 'I saw you land the whip on the mare. I was in the tower mending Danny's woolshed and he called me to the window to see Lindy on Meg. I had a grandstand view of what happened.'

Cheryl's jaw dropped slightly as the colour drained from her face. 'Scott, can't you understand why I did it? It was for us.'·

'Was it indeed?' His voice became hard. 'Well, I'm afraid that doesn't cut any ice with me. Now then, you will go to your room and pack your bags. Steve will drive you home and there'll be the devil to pay if he ever brings you back to Whitecliffs.'

She gave a gasp of dismay then whimpered, 'You can't mean it? Why are you doing this to me? Why send me away?'

'Because Lindy and I are going to be married and I doubt that she'll want to see you about the place. Now please go.'

Lindy felt dazed as she listened to his last words. They were to be *married*? But he hadn't even asked her. Perhaps she'd imagined he'd uttered those words. Perhaps she'd hit her head on the ground and her mind had gone haywire. She knew that Cheryl had given a strangled shriek and was now running back to the house, and she knew that Scott had lifted her over the fence. Nor did she protest when he picked her up and carried her across the paddock.

Half an hour later Lindy had spent time lying in a hot bath. The water had come up to her neck and the soothing heat had helped to relieve her jarred ribs and shoulders, and her arms which had taken the weight of her fall. The sound of a revving motor had come through the main bathroom window and she knew that Cheryl and her suitcases had departed in Steve's car.

The knowledge added a further sense of relief, but with it came questions concerning the statement Scott had made when he'd said they were to be married. *Married*, without having proposed to her? Or had he seen this as a rapid way of cutting his alliance with Cheryl? Yes, of course, that was it.

Doubts filled her as she towelled herself dry, nor did they abate as she dressed and applied a touch of make-up. But at least he would have to make an explanation, she told herself as she went along the passage towards the lounge.

He was waiting for her, a tall figure standing before the open fire with his legs apart. The handsome face was serious and his dark grey eyes surveyed her anxiously as his hand on her arm drew her nearer the blaze. 'How do you feel?' he asked.

'Shaken,' she admitted. 'Not only by the fall but by other things.'

As though reading her thoughts he said, 'I did mean it, you know. I hope you understand that I'm serious about this.'

But it wasn't enough. 'Mean what?' she asked innocently.

'That we're to be married, of course.'

'Oh? *Really?* I didn't know. I mean, I haven't been *asked.*'

'I'm asking you now. I love you, Lindy. I can't tell you how much. I want you to marry me.'

Her spirits took an upward leap but she remained calm. 'You could've fooled me. I was sure it was Cheryl, otherwise why was she here, riding beside you day after day?'

'She was my armour, my guard against you. Danger was written on the wall the first time I kissed you.'

She was puzzled. '*Danger?* I don't understand.'

'The danger of becoming emotionally involved. I've been fighting against it for years. So when Steve arrived home with Cheryl I decided she could act as a diversion. Her function was to keep my thoughts away from you, but in this she failed miserably.'

'And now?' Her hazel eyes were full of questions.

'Now I've given up the fight. I can't live without you and I don't intend to try.' His arms were about her, holding her gently.

Her head against his shoulder, she said, 'Didn't you say you have a job for me to fill?'

'Yes. It's the job of loving me, the job of being my wife, of being mistress of Whitecliffs.'

She laughed. 'I love that old-fashioned title.'

'Then you'll marry me as soon as possible?' His voice had become husky with an urgency he made no attempt to hide.

She nodded, her heart singing with happiness as she

lifted her face for his kiss.

'Tell me you love me,' he murmured.

'I thought you knew. I was afraid it was written all over me, that it shouted aloud every time I responded to your kisses.'

'Tell me,' he insisted.

'I love you, my darling,' she whispered.

His lips trailed from her brow to her mouth, then followed a course to a vulnerable pulse in her neck. 'My dearest, I want to crush you to me, but I'm afraid of hurting those poor bruised ribs.

'They won't be sore for ever,' she assured him.

'I'll make up for it then,' he promised. 'Perhaps it's just as well I'm being held at bay for the present. When can we be married?' he pleaded.

'As soon as Mother can make arrangements. She'll insist upon having a say in the matter.'

Ellie's voice spoke from behind them. 'I should think so. Am I right in assuming there'll be a wedding?' She looked from Scott to Lindy, her face beaming.

'You're right, as usual,' Scott smiled.

'Good. I'd better do some reading.'

They looked at her, puzzled. 'Reading?' Scott asked.

'My recipe books. I really would like to make the wedding cake.'

She left them to plan their future beside the warmth of the fire. For Lindy winter at Whitecliffs was over, but spring was about to begin.

From the author of Gypsy comes a spellbinding romance.

Unresistingly drawn into Rand's arms, Merlyn then had to suffer his rejection, as he retreated into his own private torment where he still grieved the loss of his beautiful and talented wife, Suzie.

How would Merlyn then persuade him that she would be right to play Suzie in a film based on the actress's life?

It took an unseen hand to make Rand aware of Merlyn's own special kind of magic.

ANOTHER BESTSELLER FROM CAROLE MORTIMER

W⚙RLDWIDE

 **ROMANCE**

Next month's romances from Mills & Boon

Each month, you can choose from a world of
variety in romance with Mills & Boon. These are
the new titles to look out for next month.

STANDING ON THE OUTSIDE Lindsay Armstrong
DARK ENCHANTMENT Helen Bianchin
THE DECEPTION TRAP Ann Charlton
DON'T ASK ME NOW Emma Darcy
IMMUNE TO LOVE Claudia Jameson
A REASON FOR MARRIAGE Penny Jordan
CONTRASTS Rowan Kirby
A LONG WAY FROM HEAVEN Susanne McCarthy
BRITTANY'S CASTLE Leigh Michaels
JUNGLE ISLAND Kay Thorpe
*__DIAMOND VALLEY__ Margaret Way
*__PASSION'S DAUGHTER__ Sara Wood

Buy them from your usual paperback stockist, or
write to: Mills & Boon Reader Service, P.O. Box 236,
Thornton Rd, Croydon, Surrey CR9 3RU, England.

*These two titles are available *only* from Mills & Boon
Reader Service.

Mills & Boon
the rose of romance

Merry Christmas one and all.

CHANCES ARE *Barbara Delinsky*	THE GIFT OF HAPPINESS *Amanda Carpenter*
ONE ON ONE *Jenna Lee Joyce*	HAWK'S PREY *Carole Mortimer*
AN IMPRACTICAL PASSION *Vicki Lewis Thompson*	TWO WEEKS TO REMEMBER *Betty Neels*
A WEEK FROM FRIDAY *Georgia Bockoven*	YESTERDAY'S MIRROR *Sophie Weston*

More choice for the Christmas stocking. Two special reading pack
from Mills & Boon. Adding more than a touch of romance to the
festive season.

AVAILABLE: OCTOBER, 1986   PACK PRICE: £4.80   Mills & Boon